Revision Questions for Higher Physics

Lyn Robinson

Principal Teacher of Physics
Williamwood High School, Clarkston

Editorial assistance by

Andrew McGuigan

Principal Teacher of Physics
St Kentigern's Academy, Bathgate

with some help from

Mary Webster

Published by
Chemcord
Inch Keith
East Kilbride
Glasgow

ISBN   1 870570 73 1

Printed by Bell and Bain, Glasgow

Contents

Kinematics

Exercise 1.1   Vectors and Scalars

1. a) What is meant by a vector quantity?
    b) What is meant by a scalar quantity?

2. Divide each of the following groups into vector quantities and scalar quantities.
    a) mass, weight, momentum, velocity, acceleration and kinetic energy
    b) force, mass, distance, momentum, weight
    c) velocity, power, speed, work, potential energy, displacement
    d) pressure, force, impulse, power, time, temperature

3. Decide whether each of the following statements is true or false.
    a) Scalar quantities have direction only.
    b) Vector quantities have both magnitude and direction.
    c) Speed is a vector quantity and velocity is a scalar quantity.
    d) Force and weight are vector quantities but mass is a scalar quantity.
    e) Displacement and speed are vector quantities but time is a scalar quantity.

4. A car travels from **X** to **Y** a distance of 40 km.
    Then it travels from **Y** to **Z**, a distance of 30 km as shown.
    Travelling from **X** to **Y** takes a time of 1 hour.
    Travelling from **Y** to **Z** also takes 1 hour.

    a) Calculate the final displacement of the car.
    b) Calculate the average speed of the car for the journey.
    c) Calculate the average velocity of the car for the journey.

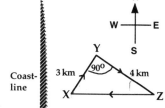

5. A yacht follows the course shown during a race.
    The race starts and finishes at **X**.

    a) Calculate the displacement of the yacht from
       position **X** when it is at posi ion **Z**.
    b) Calculate the distance trave ed by the
       yacht during the race.

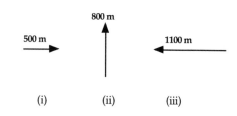

6. During part of an orienteering event
    a competitor completes the three
    displacements shown in 10 minutes.

    For the competitor for this part
    of the event, calculate
    a) the resultant displacement,
    b) the average speed,
    c) the average velocity.

7. In an orienteering competition, the competitors are given the following instructions. From the start, travel due north for 750 m, then travel due west for 1.25 km, then north east for 500 m.
   a) For a competitor who has followed the instructions, draw a scale diagram to find the displacement from the start.
   b) What direction should the competitor take to return directly to the start?

8. A boy, sitting on the back of a truck which is travelling north at 4 m s⁻¹, throws a ball at a speed of 5 m s⁻¹ across the truck in the direction indicated by arrow **XY**.

   Calculate the magnitude and direction of the velocity of the ball with respect to the ground.

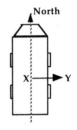

9. A canal boat is travelling with a velocity of 2.0 m s⁻¹ due west along a canal. A girl runs with a speed of 4.8 m s⁻¹ from **X** to **Y** across the deck of the boat as shown.

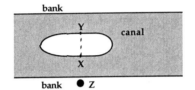

   By drawing a scale diagram or otherwise, find the resultant velocity of the girl relative to someone at point **Z** on the bank of the canal.

10. A ferry crosses from a point **A** on the mainland to a point **B** on a nearby island as shown.

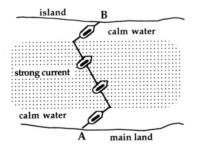

   The ferry sets out at 2.4 m s⁻¹ in the direction 40° east of north (040°).
   A strong current flowing in the middle of the channel causes the ferry to move at the same speed in the direction 40° west of north (320°), although the ferry is still pointing in the original direction as indicated in the diagram.
   On reaching the calm water near the island, the ferry continues with its original speed and direction.

   Use a vector diagram to find the velocity of the current in the middle part of the channel.

11. A ball rolls down a ramp which is inclined at 60° to the vertical as shown. When it reaches **Y** it has a velocity of 20 m s⁻¹ down the ramp.

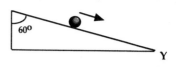

   a) Calculate the horizontal component of velocity at point **Y**.

   b) Calculate the vertical component of velocity at point **Y**.

12. During flight, a golf ball has a velocity of 50 m s⁻¹ at 40° to the horizontal as shown.

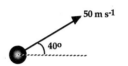

   a) Calculate the horizontal component of velocity.

   b) Calculate the vertical component of velocity.

13. A box of weight 200 N is placed on a slope of 30° to the horizontal as shown.

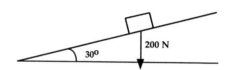

   a) Calculate the component of the weight acting down the slope.

   b) Calculate the component of the weight acting at right angles to the slope.

14. A trolley is given a push so that it rises up a steep incline as shown. It comes to a stop and then rolls back down the incline. There is a large frictional force between the trolley and the surface of the slope.

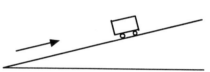

   Sketch the velocity-time graph for the motion.

Exercise 1.2   Velocity and Acceleration Graphs

1. Accurately draw the corresponding acceleration-time graph for each of the following velocity-time graphs.
    (Numerical values are required on both axes.)

a)

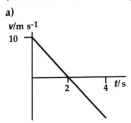

b)

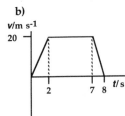

c)

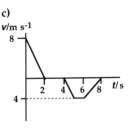

2. The velocity-time graph for the vertical component of the velocity of an object thrown upwards from ground level and then falling onto the roof of a building is shown.

    Calculate the height of the building.
    (Take the acceleration due to gravity to be 10 m s^{-2}.)

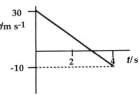

3. The graph shows how the force applied to an object of mass 5 kg varies with time. The object is initially at rest.

    Accurately draw the corresponding acceleration-time and velocity-time graphs.
    (Numerical values are required on both axes.)

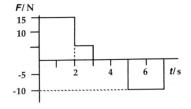

4. The velocity-time graphs for two train journeys along a straight section of track are shown.

a)

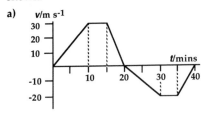

b)

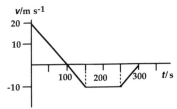

    For each train journey, calculate
    i)   the distance travelled by the train,
    ii)   the final displacement of the train,
    iii) the average velocity of the train.

5. Information can be obtained from velocity-time and acceleration-time graphs using either the gradient of the line or the area under the line.
   a) What information can be calculated from the gradient of a line on a velocity-time graph?
   b) What information can be calculated from the area under a line on a velocity-time graph?
   c) What information can be calculated from the area under the line on an acceleration-time graph?

6. The speed-time graph of a vehicle, which moves for a time of 25 s, is shown.

   Calculate the average speed of the vehicle during the 25 s.

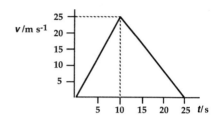

7. The acceleration-time graph of an object starting from rest is shown.

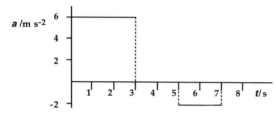

   a) What is the velocity after 6 s?
   b) What is the velocity after 8 s?

8. A ball is thrown vertically upwards at 25 m s^{-1} from ground level. When it falls to the ground it bounces several times before coming to rest.

   Sketch a velocity-time graph to represent the motion of the ball from the instant it leaves the thrower's hand until it hits the ground for a second time.

9. The graph below represents the motion of a body falling freely from rest in a vacuum.

   The quantity plotted on the **y** axis could be:

   A. speed   B. distance   C. acceleration   D. force   E. kinetic energy

10. Describe what is happening to the acceleration over each marked interval on the velocity-time graph.

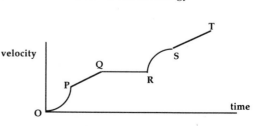

11. The speed-time graph shown is obtained for a trolley of mass 2 kg moving in a straight line.

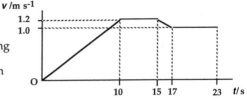

   a) Accurately draw the corresponding acceleration-time graph. (Numerical values are required on both axes.)
   b) Accurately draw the force-time graph, showing how the resultant force on the trolley varies with time. (Numerical values are required on both axes.)
   c) Describe how the motion during the first 3 s could be produced.
   d) Suggest a possible cause for the change in the speed which occurs at a time of 15 s.
   e) Calculate the total distance travelled during the 23 s of the motion.
   f) Calculate the average speed during the 23 s of the motion.

12. An object moves from rest with a constant acceleration.

   a) Sketch the acceleration-time graph.
   b) Sketch the velocity-time graph.
   c) Sketch the kinetic energy-time graph.

13. The graph shows how the acceleration of a rocket in outer space changed during a 10 s period. The rocket motors provided a constant thrust of 6×10^5 N.

   What mass of fuel was used during this 10 s period?

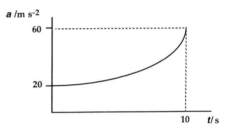

14. A space probe of mass 750 kg lifts off from the surface of a planet. The engine of the probe produces a constant thrust. The probe is rising vertically from the surface of the planet when its engine suddenly cuts out. The graph shows how the velocity of the probe varies with time from the instant of lift off until the probe crashes on the planet.

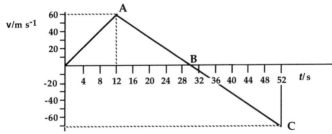

   a) Describe what is happening to the probe 12 s, 30 s and 52 s after lift off, i.e. at points A, B and C on the velocity-time graph.
   b) Find the greatest height above the planet's surface.
   c) Calculate the acceleration due to gravity on the planet.
   d) Calculate the height above or below the planet's surface of the final crash site.
   e) In reality the mass of the probe would decrease as fuel is burnt, although the force exerted by the engine remains constant.
   Sketch a graph to show how the velocity might change with time in this case.
   Mark the points corresponding to points A, B and C mentioned in part a).

15. An artificial hare travels along a straight section of track at a constant speed of 14 m s^{-1}. A dog with a reaction time of 0.4 s is released at the instant the hare passes the starting line. The dog accelerates at a constant rate for 2.5 s and reaches a speed of 15 m s^{-1}. This speed is maintained for 7.5 s after which the dog decelerates at a rate of 0.5 m s^{-2} until it has covered 200 m.

    a) Draw an accurate acceleration-time graph for the dog, including numerical values on each axis.

    b) Draw an accurate velocity-time graph for the dog, including numerical values on each axis.

    c) Calculate the time taken for the hare to reach the 200 m mark.

    d) Calculate the time taken for the dog to reach the 200 m mark.

    e) Explain whether or not the dog catches the hare.

16. A velocity-time graph of a bouncing ball is shown.

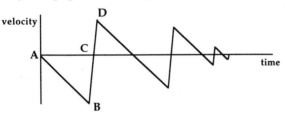

    a) Describe the motion over **AB**, **BC** and **CD**.

    b) State the number of bounces before the ball comes to rest.

    c) Explain whether or not kinetic energy is lost at each bounce.

Exercise 1.3   Equations of Motion

1. A car accelerates uniformly from 15 m s^{-1} at 2.75 m s^{-2} for 4 s.
    Calculate the final speed.

2. A boy drops a stone down a dry well. The stone strike the bottom after 3 s.
    Calculate the depth of the well? (Assume air resistance is negligible.)

3. A rocket is fired from rest up a ramp of length 3.6 m.
    It reaches a velocity of 120 m s^{-1} at the top.
    Calculate the average acceleration.

4. A car travelling at 30 m s^{-1} starts to brake when it is 50 m from a stationary lorry.
    The car moves in a straight line and manages to stop just before reaching the lorry.
    Calculate the deceleration of the car.

5. A car accelerates uniformly from rest and travels a distance of 60 m in 6.0 s.
    Calculate the acceleration of the car.

6. A car travelling at 20 m s^{-1}, accelerates uniformly at 0.5 m s^{-2} until it is travelling at
    30 m s^{-1}.
    Calculate the distance travelled by the car.

7. A car is travelling at 25 m s^{-1}.
    The brakes are applied for 5 s and the speed is reduced to 15 m s^{-1}.
    How far does the car travel in this time, if the deceleration is uniform?

8. A cargo ship travels a distance of 12 km as it decelerates uniformly to rest from a
    speed of 8.0 m s^{-1}.
    Calculate the deceleration of the ship.

9. A ball is dropped from a height of 1.25 m.
    How long does it take to reach the ground? (Assume air resistance is negligible.)

10. A car reaches a speed of 18 m s^{-1} after accelerating at 2.3 m s^{-2} for 7 s.
    Calculate its initial speed.

11. A rocket accelerates from 120 m s^{-1} at 75 m s^{-2} and travels a distance of 400 m while
    accelerating.
    Calculate the final speed of the rocket.

12. A boy runs 35 m accelerating uniformly from 2 m s^{-1} to 7 m s^{-1}.
    How long does it take him to cover this distance?

13. A suitcase is dropped from a window 11.25 m high.
    Assuming air resistance is negligible, how long does it take to reach the ground?

14. A balloonist, rising at a constant speed of 15 m s^{-1}, drops a sandbag overboard.

    Assuming that the air resistance of the sandbag is negligible, how long does it take to return to the height at which it was released?

15. In the equation $s = ut + \frac{1}{2}at^2$, what quantity does the term ut represent?

16. The following velocity-time graphs are for objects moving in a straight line.

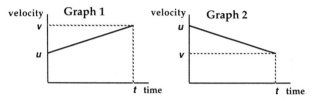

    a) Using graph 1, show that $s = ut + \frac{1}{2}at^2$

    b) Using graph 2, show that $s = \frac{1}{2}(u + v)t$

17. A helicopter is descending vertically at a constant speed of 5 m s^{-1}. A box is dropped from the helicopter. The box hits the ground 5 s later.

    How far does the box fall? (Assume air resistance is negligible.)

18. A helicopter is ascending vertically at a constant speed of 5 m s^{-1}. A box is dropped from the helicopter. The box hits the ground 5 s later.

    How far does the box fall? (Assume air resistance is negligible.)

19. A man is standing in a steep-sided canyon closer to one side-wall than the other. He shouts and hears two echos. The first echo is heard 2 s after the shout and the second echo 6 s after the shout.

    What is the width of the canyon? (Take the speed of sound to be 340 m s^{-1}.)

20. A lift is rising vertically with a constant speed of 2 m s^{-1}. A book is dropped from the lift and hits the ground 3 s later.

    Assuming the resistance due to air is negligible, calculate the height of the lift at the instant the book was dropped.

21. A boy drops a stone down a dry well and observes the stone strike the bottom after 2 s. He repeats the experiment, some time later, when there is water in the well and observes the stone hit the water after 1 s.

    How full is the well when he drops the second stone?

    A. $\frac{1}{5}$ full B. $\frac{1}{4}$ full C. $\frac{1}{2}$ full D. $\frac{3}{4}$ full E. $\frac{4}{5}$ full

22. Take the acceleration due to gravity on Earth to be 10 m s^{-2} and 26 m s^{-2} on another planet. On Earth a ball released from rest takes 0.5 s to drop through a certain height.

    Assuming that the resistance of the atmospheres can be neglected in both cases, the time in seconds for the ball to drop from rest through the same height on the other planet would be:

    A. $0.5 \times \frac{10}{26}$ B. $0.5 \times \frac{26}{10}$ C. $0.5 \times \sqrt{\frac{10}{26}}$ D. $0.5 \times \sqrt{\frac{26}{10}}$ E. $0.5 \times \left(\frac{10}{26}\right)^2$

Exercise 1.4   Projectiles - Horizontal Projection

1. A ball is projected horizontally with a speed of 40 m s⁻¹ from the top of a cliff as shown.
   What is the velocity of the ball 3 s after it leaves the edge of the cliff?
   (Assume air resistance is negligible.)

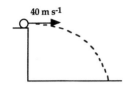

2. A plane flying horizontally at a speed of 180 m s⁻¹ over the sea releases a package. The plane is flying at a height of 245 m. Air resistance may be neglected.

   a) Find the final vertical speed of the package just before entering the sea.
   b) Draw velocity-time graphs, including numerical values on both axes, for
      i)   the horizontal velocity component of the package as it falls,
      ii) the vertical velocity component of the package as it falls.

3. A ball is thrown horizontally with a velocity v, from the top of a cliff. It takes 2 s to strike the water below and it enters the water at 45° to the horizontal.
   What is the initial velocity v of the ball?
   (Assume that the acceleration due to gravity is 10 m s⁻² and that the air resistance is negligible.)

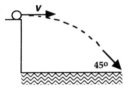

4. A ball is projected horizontally with a velocity of 30 m s⁻¹ from the top of a high tower. Air resistance may be neglected.
   After what time will its velocity be in the direction 45° to the horizontal?

5. A ball is thrown horizontally at 15 m s⁻¹ from the top of a vertical cliff and reaches the ground 45 m from the foot of the cliff.

   a) Draw accurate graphs, with the appropriate numerical scales, of
      i)   the horizontal speed of the ball against time,
      ii) the vertical speed of the ball against time, from the time it is thrown until it hits the ground.
   b) By using a vector diagram or otherwise, find the velocity of the ball 2 s after it is thrown, giving both the speed and direction. State any assumptions you have made.
   c) What are the main energy transformations which take place from the time the ball is thrown until the ball is at rest?

6. An object attached to a parachute falls from a helicopter which is hovering at a height of 120 m above point X. The object falls with a constant vertical velocity of 12 m s⁻¹. A steady side-wind gives the object a constant horizontal component of velocity of 5 m s⁻¹.

   How far from point X does the object hit the ground?

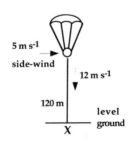

7. A tennis player hits a ball horizontally from a height of 2.4 m as shown. The ball has an initial horizontal velocity **v** (diagram **not** to scale).

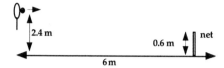

The ball just passes over the net which is 0.6 m high. The net is 6 m away from the tennis player. Neglect the effect of air resistance.

a) Calculate the time taken for the ball to reach the net.
b) What was the speed of the ball as it left the racquet?

8. In a film stunt a car is driven horizontally off a river bank and lands on the far bank. The left hand bank is 0.45 m above the right hand bank as shown.

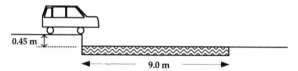

a) How long does the car spend in the air during this jump?
b) Calculate the minimum speed at which the car must be driven in order to reach the far side of the river safely. (Neglect the effect of air resistance.)

9. A motorcross rider takes a jump from a height of 1.25 m. He lands 10 m from the base of the jump.

Assuming that he was travelling horizontally when he left the edge of the jump and that air resistance can be ignored, at what speed did he approach the jump?

10. A stunt motorcyclist attempts to jump a river which is 5 m wide. The bank from which he will take off is 2 m higher than the bank on which he will land.

What is the minimum horizontal speed he must achieve just before take-off to avoid landing in the river?

11. A ball rolls down a smooth ramp and off a table as shown. The bottom of the ramp is 1.25 m above the floor.

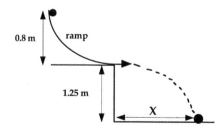

a) What is the speed of the ball at the bottom of the ramp?
b) How long does the ball take to reach the floor from the moment it leaves the ramp?
c) Calculate the distance X.

Exercise 1.5   Projectiles - Oblique Projection

1. A shell is fired from a gun and leaves the gun with a
    velocity of 160 m s⁻¹.
    The barrel of the gun is inclined at an angle of 20° to
    the horizontal as shown.
    The effect of air resistance may be ignored.

    a) Calculate the horizontal component of the velocity.
    b) Calculate the vertical component of the velocity.
    c) How long does it take the shell to reach its maximum height?
    d) How long is the shell in the air?
    e) Calculate the horizontal range of the shell.

2. An archer fires an arrow at a target 60 m distant.   28 m s⁻¹
    The arrow leaves her bow at 28 m s⁻¹ at an angle of 25° to
    the horizontal as shown.

    a) What is the horizontal component of the velocity of the arrow?
    b) How long does the arrow take to reach the target?

3. A ball is projected from point **O** with a velocity of 17 m s⁻¹ as shown.

    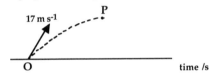

    It reaches its maximum height at **P** after 1.5 s.

    a) Calculate the initial vertical component of the velocity of the ball.
    b) Calculate the initial horizontal component of the velocity of the ball.

4. A shell of mass 200 g is launched with a velocity of 40 m s⁻¹ at 25° to the horizontal.

    a) Calculate the horizontal component of the velocity.
    b) Calculate the vertical component of the velocity.
    c) Calculate the minimum kinetic energy of the shell, stating where it occurs.
    d) When the shell is at its maximum height, state its
        i)   vertical acceleration,
        ii) horizontal acceleration.
    e) How long does the shell take to reach its maximum height?
    f) How long is the shell in the air?
    g) Calculate the horizontal range of the shell.
    h) Sketch graphs of
        i)   the horizontal component of velocity against time,
        ii) the vertical component of velocity against time.

5. A projectile fired at an angle of 45° to the horizontal has an initial vertical component
    of velocity of 30 m s⁻¹.

    What is the maximum height reached by the projectile?
    (Assume air resistance is negligible.)

6. A golf ball is struck with velocity **v** from **A** at an angle α to a horizontal site. It returns to the ground at position **R**. There is a tree 30 m tall midway between **A** and **R**.

The horizontal and vertical components of its velocity, throughout its trajectory, are shown in the graphs.

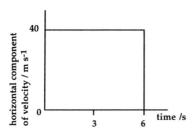
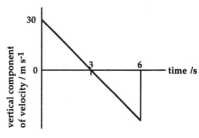

a) How far from **A** is the ball when it hits the ground at **R**?
b) By what distance does the ball clear the top of the tree?
c) Calculate the initial velocity of the ball (magnitude and direction).

7. A tennis player strikes the ball just above the surface of the tennis court and the ball reaches its maximum height of 10 m just over the net.

What is the maximum time that the second player has to get into position to play the ball before it hits the ground?

8. A ball **A** is projected from **X** at an angle of 30°
to the horizontal as shown.

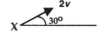

a) If air resistance is negligible, at what angle does the ball strike the ground?
b) A second identical ball **B** is projected vertically upwards with velocity **v**.
   i)   How does the time taken for **B** to hit the ground compare with the time for ball **A** to hit the ground?
   ii) Which ball has the greatest vertical deceleration?
   iii) Which ball reaches the greatest height?
c) If air resistance cannot be ignored, where in its path would ball **A** have its greatest kinetic energy?

9. An archer fires an arrow at a target which is 30 m away. The arrow is fired horizontally from a height of 1.5 m and leaves the bow with a velocity of 100 m s^{-1}. The bottom of the target is 0.9 m from the ground and the top of the target is 1.2 m from the ground.

Show by calculation whether the arrow hits the target.

10. During a visit to the Moon, an astronaut fires a small experimental projectile across a
level surface. The projectile is launched from point **P** at a speed of 24.0 m s^{-1} and an
angle of 60° to the horizontal. The projectile lands 26.0 s later at point **X**.

a) Calculate the horizontal speed of the projectile at point **P**.
b) Calculate the horizontal distance from **P** to **X**.
c) Calculate the acceleration due to gravity on the Moon.

11. A sailor has to pass a message onto the pier which is higher than the deck of his ship.
He kicks a small ball with the message inside onto the pier as shown (diagram is **not**
to scale). The ball lands at point **X**.

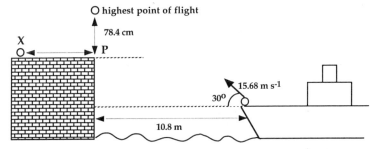

a) Calculate the horizontal component of velocity.
b) Calculate the vertical component of velocity.
c) Show that the ball is in flight for 1.2 s.
d) Find the distance **XP** along the pier if the ship is 10.8 m from the pier.

12. A stunt rider attempts to leap a number of cars, each of length 4 m, using identical
ramps as shown.

His motor cycle leaves the first ramp at **P** travelling at 24 m s^{-1} and lands at **Q** on the
second ramp. Take the acceleration due to gravity to be 10 m s^{-2} and assume air
resistance is negligible.

a) Calculate the horizontal component of velocity of the rider.
b) Calculate the vertical component of velocity of the rider.
c) Calculate the total time of flight from **P** to **Q**.
d) What is the greatest number of cars the rider could clear if the cars are parked nose
to tail?

Dynamics

Exercise 2.1   Forces

1. For each of the following, calculate the resultant force required to produce the motion described.

    a) a 400 kg car accelerating at 2.5 m s^{-2}
    b) a 200 kg rocket moving upwards from Earth at a constant speed of 38 m s^{-1}
    c) a 750 g toy car which reaches a speed of 7.5 m s^{-1} from rest in 3 s
    d) a stationary hot air balloon of mass 300 kg, carrying a total mass of 250 kg

2. A block of weight 1500 N is dragged along a horizontal surface at constant speed by a horizontal force of 500 N.

    What is the force of friction acting on the block?

3. On a certain planet the gravitational force on a mass of 2 kg is 24 N.

    If a mass of 4 kg is allowed to fall freely on that planet, what is its acceleration?

4. The forces shown act on the trolley of mass 2 kg which is originally at rest on a level surface. After 3 s the 7 N force is removed.

    a) Draw an accurate velocity-time graph for the first 3 s of the motion. (Numerical values are required on both axes.)
    b) Extend the graph accurately to show the motion of the trolley as it comes to rest.

5. A parachutist of mass 50 kg descends towards the Earth at a constant velocity of 2 m s^{-1}.

    Calculate the upwards force acting upon him.

6. Calculate the force required to lift a mass of 5.6 kg vertically upwards from the surface of the Earth at a constant speed of 4 m s^{-1}.

7. A liquid fuelled rocket lifts off vertically upwards. The rocket has an initial mass of 10 000 kg and the engine provides a thrust of 240 kN.

    a) Sketch a diagram giving the names and sizes of each force acting on take-off.
    b) What is the initial acceleration of the rocket?
    c) If the thrust is constant, explain what happens to the acceleration of the rocket as it rises.

8. A rocket of mass 1200 kg rises vertically from a planet which has a gravitational field strength of 20 N kg^{-1}. The rocket accelerates upwards from the surface of the planet at 2 m s^{-2}.

    What force must the rocket motors produce to give this acceleration?

9. A stationary hot air balloon, of total mass 500 kg, is tethered to the ground by a single vertical rope.

    a) Sketch the balloon, mark and label all the forces acting on the balloon.
    b) When the rope is released, the balloon initially accelerates vertically upwards at 1.5 m s^{-2}. Find the magnitude of the buoyancy force.
    c) Calculate the tension in the rope **before** the balloon is released.

10. The graph shows how the speed of an electric train of mass 2.0×10^5 kg changes as it makes a journey on a horizontal track between two stations.

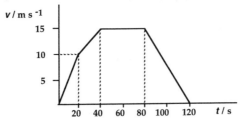

a) Draw an accurate acceleration-time graph of the train's motion. (Numerical values are required on both axes.)
b) Draw an accurate unbalanced force-time graph of the train's motion. (Numerical values are required on both axes.)

11. As part of a competition, a boy is given 1 minute to raise as many buckets of water as he can up 8 m to a window. He has to use a thin cord which breaks if the tension in it is more than 110 N. His team-mates fill the first bucket so that its total mass is 10 kg.

a) What is the greatest upwards acceleration he can give the bucket without breaking the cord? (Take *g* to be 10 m s^{-2}.)
b) Assuming the buckets all have the same mass and are always raised with the maximum acceleration, how many buckets can he lift in the minute?

12. A rocket of mass 2.2×10^6 kg is launched vertically from the surface of the Earth. The rocket engine exerts a constant force of 3.0×10^7 N.

a) Calculate the resultant force on the rocket at take-off.
b) Find the initial acceleration of the rocket as it takes off.
c) The table shows how the speed of the rocket varies at intervals of time after the launch.

t / s	0	10	20	30	40
v / m s^{-1}	0	40	90	150	220

i) What does the data in the table indicate about the acceleration of the rocket during the first 40 s of the flight?
ii) Explain what is happening to the rocket to cause this variation of speed.

13. A lunar landing craft descends vertically towards the surface of the Moon with a constant speed of 2.0 m s^{-1}. The craft and crew have a total mass of 15 000 kg. The gravitational field strength on the Moon is 1.6 N kg^{-1}.

a) During the first part of the descent the upwards thrust of the rocket is 24 kN. Show by calculation that the craft will move with a constant speed.
b) The upwards thrust of the engine is increased to 25.5 kN for the last 18 s of the descent.
i) Calculate the deceleration of the craft during this time.
ii) What is the speed of the craft just before it lands?
iii) How far above the surface of the Moon is the landing craft when the engine thrust is increased to 25.5 kN?

Exercise 2.2   Internal Forces

1. Two wooden blocks of masses 3 kg and 7 kg are in contact with each other on a frictionless horizontal surface. A horizontal force of 20 N is applied to the two blocks as shown.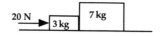

   What is the value of the horizontal force acting upon the 7 kg block?

2. A horizontal force of 10 N is applied to two blocks on a frictionless, horizontal surface as shown.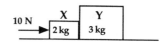

   a) What force does **X** exert on **Y**?

   b) If the 10 N force acted on the 3 kg block and in the opposite direction,
   i)   explain whether the acceleration would be the same as in part a),
   ii) calculate the horizontal force that block **Y** would exert on block **X**.

3. Two blocks, **X** and **Y**, move along a frictionless, horizontal surface at a constant velocity of 3 m s⁻¹ as shown.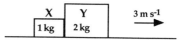

   What is the force which **X** exerts on **Y**?

4. A tractor of mass 1500 kg pulls a trailer of mass 1000 kg along a horizontal road. The total frictional force has a constant value of 4000 N. One quarter of this frictional force acts on the trailer.

   When the acceleration is 2 m s⁻², what is the force exerted on the tractor by the tow-bar?

5. Two masses are joined together by string **Y** and then hung from a beam using string **X** as shown. String **X** is burned through using a candle.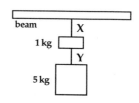

   Neglecting the mass of each string, calculate the tension in string **Y**
   a) before string **X** is burned through,
   b) after string **X** is burned through.

6. Two trolleys are joined together by a thread and are pulled along a horizontal frictionless bench by a force of 12 N. The thread at **X** breaks 3 s after starting from rest.

   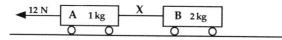

   a) Describe the motion of the two trolleys **before** the thread breaks.

   b) Describe separately the motion of trolley **A** and the motion of trolley **B after** the thread breaks.

7. Two blocks of mass 2 kg and 3 kg are joined by a long piece of elastic and moved apart on a smooth horizontal bench until the elastic is stretched considerably. Both masses are released simultaneously.

   When the 3 kg mass has moved a distance *d*, how far has the 2 kg mass travelled? (Give your answer in terms of *d*.)

Exercise 2.3   Components of Forces

1. A force of 15 N acts on a box as shown.

   a) Calculate the horizontal component of the force.
   b) Calculate the vertical component of the force.

2. A stone is about to be fired from a catapult set as shown.

   What is the magnitude of the resultant force on the stone?

3. A water skier is being towed by a rope from a boat travelling at constant speed. If the tension in the rope is 450 N as shown , calculate the force acting along the line **AB** opposing the forward motion of the skier.

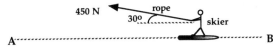

4. An acrobat is stationary at the centre of a tightrope. The angle between the rope and the horizontal is 10° as shown.

   If the acrobat weighs 600 N, calculate the tension T in the rope.

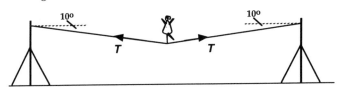

5. A volley-ball net hangs from a horizontal rope, supported by vertical poles. Each pole is anchored by a stay-wire at an angle of 30° as shown in figure **1**.

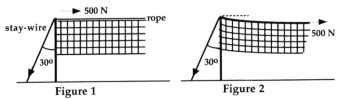

   Figure 1   **Figure 2**

   a) If the tension in the rope is 500 N, what is the tension in the stay-wire?
   b) In practice the rope will not be horizontal but will sag as shown in figure **2**. What effect will this have on the value of the tension in the stay-wire as calculated in part **a)**?

6. A 2 kg mass is hanging by a string from the roof. A horizontal force *F* is applied to hold the string in the position shown. The 2 kg mass and the string are stationary.

   By drawing a scale diagram or otherwise, find the value of *F*.

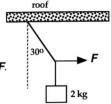

Exercise 2.4   Force on a Slope

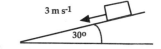

1. A block of wood of mass 2.0 kg slides down a 30° slope at 3 m s⁻¹ as shown.
    What is the value of the force of friction acting on the block?

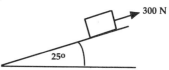

2. A mass of 10 kg is moving up an incline with a constant acceleration of 10 m s⁻². An applied force of 300 N acts up the incline as shown.
    a) Calculate the component of the weight acting down the slope.
    b) Calculate the value of the friction force acting down the slope.

3. A cyclist free-wheels down a slope inclined at 15° to the horizontal, at a constant velocity of 3 m s⁻¹. The combined mass of the rider and the bicycle is 85 kg.
    What is the force of friction acting on the bicycle and rider?

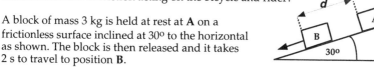

4. A block of mass 3 kg is held at rest at **A** on a frictionless surface inclined at 30° to the horizontal as shown. The block is then released and it takes 2 s to travel to position **B**.
    a) Calculate the component of the weight acting down the slope.
    b) Calculate the acceleration of the block down the slope.
    c) Find the distance *d* travelled in the 2 s.

5. A child on a sledge slides down a slope which is at an angle of 20° to the horizontal. The combined weight of the child and the sledge is 400 N. The frictional force acting on the sledge and child at the start of the slide is 20 N.
    a) i)   Calculate the component of the combined weight of the child and sledge down the slope.
       ii) Calculate the initial acceleration of the child and sledge.
    b) The child decides to start the slide further up the slope.
       Explain whether or not this has any effect on the initial acceleration.
    c) During the slide, the sledge does not continue to accelerate but reaches a constant speed.
       Explain why this happens.

Exercise 2.5   Lifts

1. A lift and passengers of total mass 2000 kg is travelling upwards at 3.9 m s^{-1}.
    The cable supporting the lift exerts an upwards force of 17 000 N.
    a) Calculate the acceleration of the lift.
    b) Calculate the time taken for the lift to stop if this acceleration continues.

2. An object of mass 1.0 kg hangs from a spring balance which is suspended on the inside
    of a small rocket. The rocket accelerates upwards from the Earth's surface at 2.0 m s^{-2}.
    What is the reading on the balance?

3. A mass of 0.060 kg is suspended from a spring balance inside a lift.
    The lift accelerates down at 4.0 m s^{-2}.
    What is the reading on the spring balance?

4. A man weighs 800 N and stands on an accurate weighing machine in a lift.
    The reading on this weighing machine is 820 N.
    Calculate the **two** possible accelerations of the lift, giving the directions of the
    acceleration.

5. A lift is raised and lowered by means of a cable. All accelerations and decelerations
    have a magnitude of 2 m s^{-2}.
    During which two parts of the lift's journey is the tension in the cable at a maximum?

6. A mass of 1.0 kg hangs from a spring balance which is attached to the roof of a lift.
    The balance has a scale marked from 0 to 25 N.
    Calculate the reading which the balance will show
    a) when the lift is at rest,
    b) when the lift is moving up at 4 m s^{-1},
    c) when the lift is accelerating up at 3 m s^{-2},
    d) when the lift is accelerating down at 2 m s^{-2},
    e) when the lift is decelerating at 4 m s^{-2} while moving down.

7. A man is standing in a lift which is initially at rest. **F** is the force which is exerted by the
    man's feet on the floor of the lift and **R** is the force exerted by the floor of the lift on
    the man's feet. For each of the following, describe how the magnitudes of **F** and **R**
    compare.
    a) The lift accelerates upwards.
    b) The lift travels upwards at a constant velocity.
    c) The lift decelerates while travelling upwards.
    d) The lift accelerates downwards.
    e) The lift decelerates while travelling downwards.

8. A student of mass 70 kg investigates the motion of a lift. He stands on a weighing
    machine in a lift on its downward journey. For 2 s immediately after the lift starts the
    weighing machine reads 560 N, then for a further 6 s it reads 700 N and for the final 2 s
    it reads 840 N.
    a) Describe the motion of the lift during its journey.
    b) Calculate the magnitude and direction of the resultant force at each stage.
    c) Draw an accurate acceleration-time graph for the journey.
        (Numerical values are required on both axes.)

Exercise 2.6   Momentum

1. Calculate the momentum of each of the following.
    a) a 700 kg van travelling to the right at 17 m s⁻¹
    b) a 1.8 kg toy bus travelling to the left at 85 cm s⁻¹
    c) a 450 g ball travelling to the left at 2.8 m s⁻¹
    d) a 1500 kg rocket travelling to the right at 8 km s⁻¹

2. A field-gun of mass 1000 kg fires a shell of mass 10 kg with velocity of 100 m s⁻¹.
    Calculate the recoil velocity of the field-gun.

3. A shell of mass 5 kg is travelling horizontally with a speed of 200 m s⁻¹ when it
    explodes into two parts. One part of mass 3 kg continues in the original direction at
    100 m s⁻¹.
    Calculate the velocity of the other part.

4. Two trolleys are moving in the same direction as shown. The trolleys collide, coupling
    together on impact.

    What is their common velocity after impact?

5. Two trolleys fitted with magnets collide as shown.

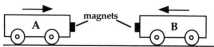

    For each of the following, calculate the velocity of the two trolleys after the collision.
    a) Trolley **A** has a mass of 2 kg and is moving at 1 m s⁻¹. Trolley **B** has a mass of 2 kg
       and is moving at 2 m s⁻¹. (The magnets stick together.)
    b) Trolley **A** has a mass of 2 kg and is moving at 3 m s⁻¹. Trolley **B** has a mass of 1.5 kg
       and is moving at 4 m s⁻¹. (The magnets stick together.)
    c) Trolley **A** has a mass of 1.5 kg and is moving at 5 m s⁻¹. Trolley **B** has a mass of 2 kg
       and is moving at 2 m s⁻¹. Trolley **A** rebounds at 3 m s⁻¹. (The magnets repel.)

6. Two linear air track vehicles, **P** and **Q**, are projected towards each other as shown.
    The masses of **P** and **Q** are 0.4 kg and 0.2 kg respectively.

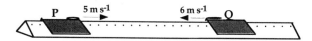

    a) Vehicle **Q** rebounds to the right with a velocity of 2 m s⁻¹.
       Calculate the velocity of vehicle **P**.
    b) Vehicle **P** rebounds to the left with a velocity of 2 m s⁻¹.
       Calculate the velocity of vehicle **Q**.

Exercise 2.7   Elastic and Inelastic Collisions

1   a) What is meant by a perfectly elastic collision?
    b) What is meant by a inelastic collision?

2. Two balls collide head-on as shown.
    The larger 4 kg ball rebounds at 1.5 m s⁻¹.
    a) Calculate the velocity of the smaller ball.
    b) Show by calculation whether the collision
       is elastic or inelastic.

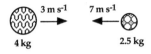

3. A ball **X** of mass 1 kg travelling at 5 m s⁻¹ strikes a stationary ball **Y** of mass 2 kg.
    Ball **X** rebounds along its original path at 1 m s⁻¹.
    a) Calculate the velocity of ball **Y**
    b) Show by calculation whether the collision is elastic or inelastic.

4. Two balls collide head-on as shown.
    The larger 4 kg ball rebounds at 1 m s⁻¹.
    a) Calculate the velocity of the smaller ball.
    b) Show by calculation whether the collision is
       elastic or inelastic.

5. A trolley of mass 2 kg moving at 2 m s⁻¹ collides inelastically with an identical
    stationary trolley. After the collision, they move off coupled together.
    How much kinetic energy is lost during the impact?

6. In the diagram shown, the blocks are of equal mass and the horizontal surface can be
    considered frictionless. When block **A**, moving at 4 m s⁻¹, moves under block **B**, block
    B is dropped onto and sticks to block **A**.

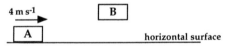

    a) Is the total momentum affected by block **B** falling on block **A**?
    b) Calculate the velocity of the combined masses after block **B** falls on block **A**.
    c) How is the total kinetic energy affected by block **B** falling on block **A**?

7. A girl on a bicycle is cycling at a constant speed. The combined kinetic energy of the
    girl and her bicycle is 1600 J. She then slows down.
    What is the new combined kinetic energy of the girl and her bicycle when their
    combined momentum is half its previous value?

Exercise 2.8   Impulse

1. Give **two** formulae for impulse and state the units for impulse in each case.

2. An unbalanced force of 60 N acts on a mass of 3.0 kg.

    If the force acts for a time of 0.10 s, calculate the impulse given to the mass.

3. A car with a mass of 600 kg and a velocity of 40 m s^{-1} skids and crashes into a wall. The car comes to a rest 50 ms after hitting the wall.

    a) Calculate the change in momentum of the car.
    b) Calculate the average force on the car during the crash.

4. A ball of mass 1 kg is initially at rest. The ball is kicked and moves off with a velocity of 10 m s^{-1}.

    If the impact between the boot and the ball lasts for 125 ms, calculate the average force exerted on the ball.

5. The graph shows how the force **F** exerted on a body varies with time **t**.

    What is represented by the area under the graph?

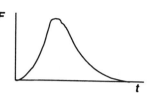

6. The graphs show how the force exerted on a body varies with time. The body has a mass of 2 kg and is initially at rest.

    In each case, calculate the speed of the body after 4 s.

    a)   **b)**   **c)**

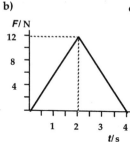 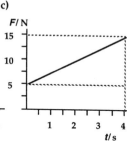

7. The graph shows how the force applied to an object of mass 5 kg varies with time. The object is initially at rest.

    a) Sketch the matching acceleration-time graph.
    b) Sketch the matching velocity-time graph.

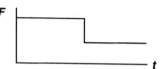

8. A motorcycle safety helmet has a soft inner lining which is compressed on impact during an accident.

    Explain how the design protects the skull.

9. During a discussion on football, a pupil claims that the time of contact between boot and ball is approximately 20 ms. He further claims that the speed of the ball leaving the boot is about 10 m s^{-1}.
   a) Clearly describe experiments which could be carried out in the laboratory to test **both** these claims. Your description should include
      i)   a labelled diagram of the apparatus used,
      ii)   the experimental procedure,
      iii) the measurements made.
   b) Indicate how you would calculate the average force of impact during the kick, stating any additional information required for this calculation.

10. A stationary snooker ball of mass 200 g is hit by a cue so that the ball moves off with an initial velocity of 2 m s^{-1}. The time of contact between the cue and the ball is measured electronically to be 50 ms.
    Calculate the average force exerted on the ball by the cue.

11. A golfer hits a golf ball of mass 5.0 x 10^{-2} kg into the air. The club is in contact with the ball for 0.5 ms. The average force exerted on the ball during contact with the club is 3.0 x 10^3 N.
    Calculate the resulting speed of the ball immediately after being struck.

12. A window is to be designed so that it is strong enough to withstand the force produced by a wind blowing at 50 m s^{-1}. In order to estimate the force exerted by the wind on the window, it is assumed that the air strikes the window at right angles and is brought to rest by the collision.
    a) If the window is rectangular with length 2.00 m and breadth 1.50 m, calculate the volume of air brought to rest in 1 s by the window when the wind speed is 50 m s^{-1}.
    b) Calculate the mass of this air, taking the density of air as 1.29 kg m^{-3}.
    c) Calculate the force on the glass when the wind is blowing at 50 m s^{-1}.

13. The bar graph indicates how the force of a golf club on a golf ball varies with time. The golf ball has a mass of 0.046 kg.

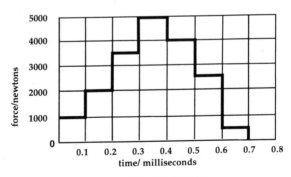

   a) Show that the total impulse on the golf ball is 1.85 N s.
   b) State the change in momentum of the golf ball.
   c) Calculate the speed of the golf ball as it leaves the club.

14. A projectile is fired horizontally from a vehicle initially at rest on a linear air track.

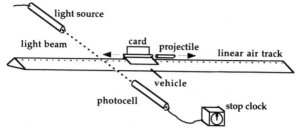

The stop clock is operated as the card on the vehicle passes through the light beam. The following data is collected.

Mass of vehicle = 0.36 kg
Length of card = 0.10 m
Time for card to pass through beam = 0.18 s

a) Calculate the speed of the vehicle after firing the projectile.
b) Calculate the impulse exerted on the vehicle.

15. A rocket motor ejects burnt fuel in the form of high speed exhaust gases.

a) Explain how this propels the rocket forward by making clear reference to a principle or law of physics.
b) At a particular time the rocket ejects 1500 kg of burnt fuel per second at an average speed of 3000 m s^{-1} relative to the rocket.
i) Calculate the change in momentum of the burnt fuel as it is ejected.
ii) Calculate the force exerted on the rocket at this time.
iii) The force of the rocket motor remains constant for a time but the acceleration of the rocket changes. Explain.

16. During a game of hockey, a stationary ball of mass 150 g is struck by a player. The graph shows how the force on the ball varies with time.

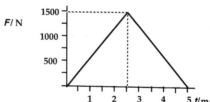

a) i) Calculate the impulse exerted on the ball.
ii) Calculate the speed with which the ball leaves the hockey stick.
b) During an indoor practice game, the same player hits a practice ball of the same mass. The practice ball is made from a softer material. The ball moves off with the same speed as before.
Sketch a graph showing how the force on the practice ball might vary with time. Indicate how this second graph compares with that shown.
c) If the same player hit a ball of mass 125 g with the same impulse, what effect will this have on the speed of the hockey ball?

Exercise 2.9   Energy

1. A golf ball is dropped on to a horizontal concrete floor. It rebounds to three-quarters of its original height.
   State in detail what energy changes take place.

2. A vehicle of total mass 1600 kg was brought to rest on a level road by applying its brakes. 5×10^5 J of heat was produced.
   What was the speed of the vehicle just before the brakes were applied?

3. A crate is pushed 10 m along a horizontal surface by a force of 80 N. The frictional force opposing the motion is 60 N.
   a) Calculate the total work done.
   b) Calculate the heat energy produced.
   c) Calculate the kinetic energy gained by the crate.

4. A catapult is extended a distance of 0.50 m. The force required to hold it in this extended position is 160 N.
   a) How much potential energy is stored in the catapult?
   b) With what velocity will a stone of mass 0.05 kg leave the catapult?
   c) State one important assumption you have made.

5. A block X of mass 3 kg is accelerated from rest by a force of 5 N for 2 s. An identical block Y is accelerated from rest by a force of 5 N for 4 s.
   What is the ratio of the kinetic energy of X to the kinetic energy of Y after accelerating?

6. A rocket of mass 1500 kg slows down from 580 m s^{-1} to 120 m s^{-1} due to friction with the atmosphere.
   How much kinetic energy does it lose?

7. The force applied to a block on a frictionless surface varies as shown in the graph.

   If the block was initially stationary and then moves in a straight line, what will be its kinetic energy after it covers a distance of 4 m?

   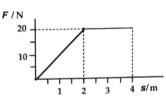

8. A pendulum bob of mass 200 g is released from position **B**, a distance **h** above the lowest position of the bob at **A**. Assume air resistance is negligible.

   Calculate the speed of the bob when it reaches **A** for
   a) i) **h** = 0.2 m,
      ii) **h** = 80 cm.
   b) What piece of information is not required in order to do the calculations in part a)?

   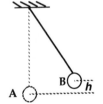

9. An object moving at 20 m s^{-1} has 500 J of kinetic energy. After undergoing an acceleration its kinetic energy increases to 2000 J.
   Calculate the new speed.

10. A rifle bullet has a speed of 320 m s⁻¹ just before it enters a fixed block of soft wood. The bullet comes to rest after penetrating 80 mm into the wood.

a) Assuming that the retarding force is constant, find the time taken for the bullet to come to rest.

b) If the bullet has a mass of 50 g, calculate the size of the retarding force.

11. The driver of a car travelling along a level road brakes sharply. The front wheels of the car lock producing the skid marks shown as the car comes to a rest.

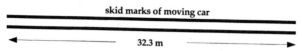

skid marks of moving car

32.3 m

The mass of the car including the driver is 1050 kg. It is estimated that the frictional force while skidding is 5210 N.

Calculate the speed of the car just before its wheels locked.

12. A trolley of mass 4.5 kg is released from rest at the top of a slope as shown. When it reaches the bottom of the slope it is travelling at 2.5 m s⁻¹.

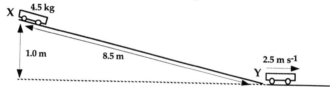

X 4.5 kg

1.0 m   8.5 m   2.5 m s⁻¹
                                                  Y

a) Calculate the potential energy of the trolley at **X**.

b) Calculate the kinetic energy of the trolley at **Y**.

c) Calculate the work done against friction while moving from **X** to **Y**.

d) If the distance **XY** is 8.5 m, calculate the average force due to friction.

13. A bullet is fired into a suspended block of wood which is able to swing freely in a vertical plane. The bullet becomes embedded in the wood and they move off together at 1.0 m s⁻¹.

Through what **vertical** height does the pendulum swing?

14. A chair-lift can carry 60 people at a time up a slope 300 m long. The slope makes an angle of 30° with the horizontal. The average mass of a person is 70 kg and the average speed of the chairs up the slope is 4 m s⁻¹.

a) What is the minimum power output of the motor required to operate the chair-lift?

b) In practice the power output of the motor would have to be greater than the value calculated.

Suggest a reason for this.

c) What happens to the kinetic energy of the chair lift while it stops to let people off?

d) Discuss the effect on the answer to part **a)** if the slope rose to the same height but made a smaller angle with the horizontal.

State clearly any assumptions made in arriving at your conclusion.

Exercise 2.10   Mechanics - Mixed Problems

1. The diagram below illustrates an experimental method which can be used to measure the speed of an air rifle pellet.

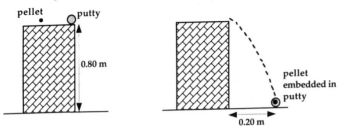

pellet   putty

0.80 m

pellet embedded in putty

0.20 m

A lump of putty of mass 0.10 kg is rested on the edge of a bench of height 0.80 m. The pellet, of mass 0.5 g, is fired at the lump of putty. The putty, with the pellet embedded in it, lands 0.20 m from the foot of the bench.

a) Show that the horizontal velocity of the putty plus pellet after the impact is 0.5 m s^{-1}.

b) State the principle of conservation of momentum.

c) Calculate the velocity of the pellet just before it strikes the putty.

d) Using only the apparatus above, suggest one way of improving the accuracy of this experiment.

2. A ball of mass 50 g is dropped from 1.25 m and bounces back to a height of 0.80 m. Take g to be 10 m s^{-2}.

a) Calculate the velocity of the ball just before collision with the ground.

b) Calculate the velocity of the ball just after collision with the ground.

c) Calculate the change in momentum of the ball.

d) If the ball is in contact with the ground for 100 ms, calculate the average force of impact with the ground.

e) Draw an accurate velocity-time graph form the start to the top of the bounce. (Numerical values are required on both axes.)

3. A golf ball of mass 46 g is launched at 40 m s^{-1} at an angle of 30° over horizontal ground.

a) Calculate the initial horizontal component of the velocity of the ball.

b) Calculate the initial vertical component of the velocity of the ball.

c) Copy and complete the table below. (Assume air resistance is negligible.)

Time/s	0	1	2
Horizontal speed/m s^{-1}			
Vertical speed/m s^{-1}			
Speed/m s^{-1}			
Kinetic energy/J			

d) Draw the graph of kinetic energy of the ball against time from the time of launch until the ball first strikes the ground.

e) Use the graph to find the potential energy gained by the ball in the first 1.5 s of flight.

4. A dart of mass 22 g is travelling at 7 m s⁻¹ when it strikes a dart board. (Assume the resistive force exerted by the material of the board is constant at 20 N.)

    a) How thick must the board be to prevent the point of the dart reaching the wall behind the board?

    b) Draw an accurate force-time graph for the motion of the dart starting 1 s before it hits the board. (Numerical values are required on both axes.)

    c) In practice the force will not be constant.
Sketch a more realistic force-time graph on the same axes.

5. A ball is released from **A** and rolls off the bench at **B**, landing at **C** as shown.

    a) Calculate the time taken to fall from **B** to **C**.

    b) Calculate the horizontal speed at **B**.

    c) Calculate the height **h** of **A** above the bench.

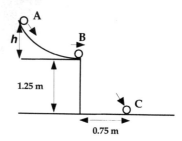

6. A rocket-propelled vehicle carrying a dummy is used at a research centre to test the ejection seat for a jet aircraft. The vehicle and dummy have a combined mass of 500 kg. The rocket engines increase the kinetic energy of the vehicle by 2.80 x 10⁷ J for each kilogram of fuel used. In a test run the vehicle accelerates from rest along the track until 0.70 kg of fuel are used up.

    a) i) Show that the maximum possible speed reached by the vehicle is 280 m s⁻¹.

    ii) What assumption have you made in part i)?

    b) The vehicle takes 8.0 s to reach this speed and then the dummy is ejected.
Calculate how far from the start the dummy is ejected.
(Assume that the acceleration is constant.)

    c) The ejection seat being tested projects the dummy upwards with an initial vertical velocity of 50 m s⁻¹.
Calculate the maximum height reached by the dummy.

7. A pile is driven into the ground by a hammer of mass 600 kg falling freely from rest through a height of 7.5 m on to the pile of mass 1800 kg. The pile and hammer then move together as the pile is driven 0.15 m into the ground from level **A** to rest at level **B**.

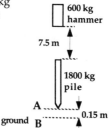

    a) Calculate the speed of the hammer just before it hits the pile.

    b) Calculate the common speed of the hammer and pile after the collision.

    c) State one assumption you must make to justify your use of the principle of conservation of momentum in part **b)**.

    d) What is the change in kinetic energy from **A** to **B**?

    e) What is the change in potential energy from **A** to **B**?

    f) What is the average force exerted by the ground on the pile as it moves from **A** to **B**?

8. On a calm day, a hot air balloon is tethered to the ground by a rope in which there is a tension of 160 N. The total weight of the balloon is 640 N.

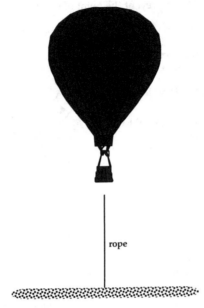

rope

a) Draw a diagram showing all the forces acting on the balloon.
b) The balloonist releases the rope which tethers the balloon to the ground.
   i)   Find the acceleration of the balloon when the rope is released.
   ii) Find the velocity of the balloon 10 s after the rope is released.
        (Assume the acceleration of the balloon is constant.)
c) The balloonist **now** accidentally drops a spanner. The spanner hits the ground after 8 s.
   i)   Describe the motion of the spanner relative to the Earth after the spanner is dropped.
   ii) Calculate the height of the balloon when the spanner is dropped.
d) Explain clearly how the balloonist could use a 1 kg mass and a spring balance to measure the vertical acceleration of the balloon.

Properties of Matter

Exercise 3.1   Density

1. 1 cm^3 of water is boiled into steam.
   What is the approximate volume of steam which is produced?

2. When a solid changes into a liquid, state the approximate change in
   a) volume,
   b) average particle spacing,
   c) density.

3. When a liquid changes into a gas, state the approximate change in
   a) volume,
   b) average particle spacing,
   c) density.

4. When a certain liquid evaporates the average spacing of the particles increases by a factor of 9.3.
   To the nearest ten, by what factor does the volume of the gas increase?

5. What is the volume of 60 g of mercury?
   (Take the density of mercury to be $13.6 \times 10^3 \text{ kg m}^{-3}$.)

6. A piece of wood with a mass of 27 g has a volume of 24 cm^3.
   Calculate its density, in kg m^{-3}.

7. The density of mercury is $13\,600 \text{ kg m}^{-3}$.
   What weight of mercury would fill a 250 cm^3 container?

8. An empty room measures 8 m x 5 m x 3 m.
   Calculate the mass of air in the room.
   (Take the density of air to be 1.23 kg m^{-3}.)

9. What volume of water will have the same weight as 1.5 litres of mercury?
   (Take the density of mercury to be $13\,600 \text{ kg m}^{-3}$ and the density of water to be 1000 kg m^{-3}.)

10. Describe an experiment which can be carried out to find the density of air.
    Your answer should include a sketch of the apparatus, a description of how the measurements are made and how the density is calculated.

11. A fixed mass of gas condenses at atmospheric pressure to form a liquid.
    By what factors do the density and the molecular spacing change?

12. Copy and complete the following table.

	Solid	Liquid	Gas
Particle separation	*d*		
Volume			
Density			

Exercise 3.2   Pressure, Force and Area

1. A solid cylinder of mass 20 kg has a flat base of area 0.1 m³ in contact with a level table. What pressure does the cylinder exert on the table?

2. A rectangular block of wood of mass 55 kg has dimensions of 2 m by 1 m by 100 cm. What is the greatest pressure that the block can exert when lying on a level surface?

3. An aircraft cruises at an altitude at which the air pressure is 4×10^4 Pa but the inside of the aircraft cabin is maintained at 1×10^5 Pa. The area of an external cabin door is 2 m². What is the outward force produced on this door?

4. A wire is used to slice cheese. The effective area of the wire in contact with the cheese is 50 mm² and the force applied is 20 N.
   Calculate the pressure applied to the cheese.

5. Three cubic blocks are arranged as shown. The dimensions and masses are given.

   a) Calculate the pressure on the top of block R.
   b) Calculate the pressure on the bench.

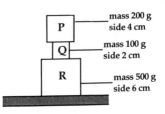

6. The leg of a tripod stand has a flat foot which makes contact with the bench over an area of 1.5 cm². The leg exerts a force of 28 N at an angle of 25° to the vertical.
   Calculate the pressure exerted by the leg.

7. a) What pressure, in pascals, is exerted by a 75 kg man standing still on the ice of a frozen pond, if each foot has an area of 280 cm²?
   b) What pressure, in pascals, is exerted by a lady wearing stiletto heels on a tiled floor? (Decide on appropriate values.)

8. The air pressure inside the passenger cabin of an airliner is 9×10^4 Pa when the airliner is at cruising height. The pressure of the outside atmosphere at this height is 4×10^4 Pa.
   Calculate the resultant force on the cabin door, of area 3 m³, caused by this difference in air pressure.

9. An elephant has a mass of 6500 kg and each of its four feet have an area of 950 cm².
   Calculate the pressure exerted when the elephant stands
   a) on all four feet,
   b) on two feet, in a circus act.

Exercise 3.3   Boyle's Law

1. **a)** State Boyle's Law, giving the **two** variables which must be kept constant.
    b) Sketch a graph showing how gas volume changes with pressure under these
    conditions.

2. Gas is contained in a cylinder of uniform cross-section
    which is fitted with a piston and a Bourdon gauge as shown.

    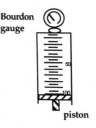

    a) When the piston is at the 100 cm mark, the gas pressure
    inside the cylinder is 3×10^5 Pa.

    What will the new pressure reading be if the piston is
    moved in to the 75 cm mark?
    (Assume that there is no change in temperature.)
    b) The gas is at a pressure of 4.5×10^5 Pa when the piston is
    at the 80 cm mark.

    What will the pressure become if the piston moves in by 16 cm?

3. An underwater swimmer uses a cylinder of compressed air. The cylinder holds 15 litres
    of air at a pressure of 14 000 kPa.

    a) Calculate the volume this air would occupy at atmospheric pressure (1×10^5 Pa).
    (Assume that there is no change in temperature.)
    b) When under water, at a depth where the total pressure is 200 kPa, the swimmer
    breathes 25 litres of air at this pressure each minute.
    Calculate the maximum length of time the swimmer could spend at this depth,
    i)   assuming that he could use all the air from the cylinder,
    ii) taking into account the air which must remain in the cylinder.

4.

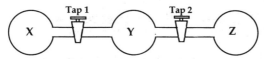

   Flasks **X**, **Y**, and **Z** have the same volumes. **X** contains air at a pressure of
   10 atmospheres while **Y** and **Z** have been evacuated and the taps are closed.
   Assume that there is no change in temperature.

   a) What will the pressure become in flask **Y** if tap **1** is opened?
   b) What will the pressure become in flask **Y** if tap **2** is then opened as well?

5. A bicycle pump has its barrel full of air at a pressure of 1.0×10^5 Pa. The pressure in the
    tyre which is to be inflated is 1.5×10^5 Pa at 20 °C.

    If the original volume of air in the barrel is 600 cm^3 and there is no temperature
    change during the movement of the piston, what will be the new volume of air in the
    pump when the tyre valve is just opening?

6. Describe an experiment which can be carried out to verify Boyle's law.
    Your answer should include
    a) a sketch of the apparatus used,
    b) the experimental procedure including the measurements taken,
    c) an indication of how the results are used to prove the law.

7. Two steel cylinders are connected by a pipe with a closed connecting tap. The volume and pressure of the gas in each cylinder is shown.

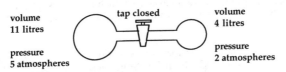

volume
11 litres

pressure
5 atmospheres

tap closed

volume
4 litres

pressure
2 atmospheres

Calculate the resulting pressure of the gas in atmospheres when the tap is opened. (Assume that the temperature of the gas remains constant.)

8. A pressure gauge for use with car tyres is calibrated so that it reads excess pressure, i.e. it read zero at normal atmospheric pressure.

If the pressure is 1.4×10^5 Pa when the volume of air is 500 cm^3, what would the pressure become if the volume drops to 460 cm^3? (Assume that the temperature of the gas remains constant.)

9. In processing photographic films the developer is agitated by bubbling nitrogen gas through it. The nitrogen is supplied by a cylinder of volume 0.06 m^3 at a pressure of 2.7×10^7 Pa. The nitrogen is released into the developer at a pressure of 1.5×10^5 Pa and at an average flow rate of 3.0×10^{-3} m^3 per minute.

Calculate the total time for which this cylinder will supply gas to the developer tank.

10. The apparatus shown was used to find the relationship between the pressure and volume of a gas.

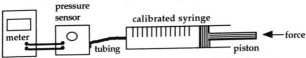

pressure
sensor

calibrated syringe

meter

tubing

force

piston

The pressure can be varied by exerting a force on the piston. The temperature is assumed to be constant and the following measurements of pressure and volume were recorded.

Pressure /kPa	100	150	200	250
Volume/cm^3	14.7	9.9	7.4	5.9

a) Using all the data, establish the relationship between the pressure and volume of the trapped air.
b) The force on the piston was then altered until the volume of the trapped air became 5.0 cm^3.
    Calculate the pressure of the trapped air.
c) The experiment was repeated with the tubing between the syringe and the pressure sensor replaced by one of longer length.
    What effect would this have on the results of the experiment?

Exercise 3.4   Pressure Law

1. a) State the relationship between the pressure and temperature of a gas.
    b) Which **two** variables must be kept constant?
    c) Sketch the graph of pressure against temperature under these conditions. Indicate suitable units for the quantities on each axis.

2. Liquid nitrogen changes to its gaseous state at a temperature of -196 °C.
    a) What is this temperature in kelvin?
    b) Explain why a temperature of 0 K is described as 'the absolute zero of temperature'.

3. A liquid is heated from 17 °C to 50 °C.
    Calculate the temperature rise
    a) in degrees celsius,
    b) in kelvin.

4. The pressure of a gas in a sealed bottle is 5×10^5 Pa at 100 °C.
    Calculate the pressure of the gas when the temperature is reduced to -10 °C.

5. On a certain day the atmospheric pressure is 1×10^5 Pa and the temperature is 7 °C. A car pressure gauge which reads 0 Pa when open to the atmosphere reads 1.24×10^5 Pa when connected to a car tyre.
    a) What is the reading on the gauge after the car has been standing in the sun until the temperature of the air in the tyre has risen to 27 °C?
    b) Sometime later the car is involved in a fire. The tyre has a weakness and will explode when the pressure inside reaches 3.6×10^5 Pa. At what temperature does this occur?

6. The apparatus shown can be used as a type of thermometer. It consists of a bulb containing helium gas, the pressure of which can be monitored. The volume of helium is assumed to remain constant.

The following results were obtained while calibrating the thermometer.

Pressure /kPa	89	96	103	110	117
Temperature/°C	-20	0	20	40	60

a) Using all the data, establish the relationship between the pressure and temperature of the helium.
b) When the bulb is immersed in a sample of liquid nitrogen, the meter gives a reading of 24 kPa for the pressure of the helium gas. Calculate the temperature of the helium sample.
c) What temperature does the data predict for absolute zero?
d) Explain how the apparatus could be used as a thermometer.

Exercise 3.5 Charles' Law

1. a) State Charles' Law, giving the **two** variables which must be kept constant.
   b) Sketch the graph of volume against temperature under these conditions.
      Indicate suitable units for the quantities on each axis.

2. A fixed mass of gas occupies 200 cm³ at 27 °C.

   Assuming the pressure remains constant, at what temperature will the volume have increased to 400 cm³?

3. At 50 °C the volume of a fixed mass of gas is 4.5 litres.

   Assuming the pressure remains constant, what will the volume of the gas be at 150 °C?

4. A graduated glass tube containing air trapped below a mercury thread is immersed in a beaker of water.

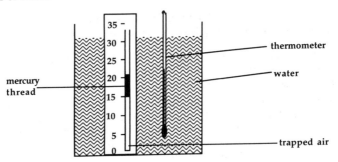

   When the temperature of the water is 27 °C, the volume of the trapped air is 0.15 cm³.
   a) Sketch a graph to shows how the volume of this trapped air, in cubic centimetres, changes with temperature, in degrees celsius.
   b) Explain how this graph can be changed in order to prove the relationship between volume and temperature.
   c) What volume does the trapped air occupy when the temperature is 77 °C?
   d) Describe how this glass tube could now be used to find the temperature, in degrees celsius, of a freezing mixture of ice and salt.
   e) Explain why the accuracy of this thermometer would be affected by a change in atmospheric pressure.

5. A balloon contains 3.5 litres of air at 27 °C. It is placed in a freezer and shrinks to a volume of 2.8 litres.
   What is the temperature inside the freezer?

6. 5 m³ of air has a pressure of 4 atmospheres and a temperature of 0 °C.

   Calculate the volume if the temperature is increased to 300 °C at the same pressure.

Exercise 3.6   General Gas Equation and the Kinetic Model

1. **a)** How does the kinetic model explain the pressure exerted by a gas?
    b) As the temperature of a gas increases, what happens to the gas particles?

2. Explain each of the following in terms of the kinetic model.

    a) For a constant volume of gas, the pressure increases when the temperature of the gas increases.
    b) For a constant pressure of gas, the volume increases when the temperature increases.
    c) At a constant temperature, the pressure of a gas increases when the volume decreases.

3. Explain, in terms of the kinetic model, what happens to the pressure of a gas when
    a) the temperature decreases but the volume remains constant,
    b) the volume increases but the temperature remains constant.

4. After a car has been parked in the sun for some time, it is found that the pressure in the tyres has increased.

    Stating any assumptions that are made, explain in terms of the kinetic model why the pressure increases.

5. 100 cm^3 of gas at 27 ^{o}C is heated to 54 ^{o}C without any change of pressure.

    Calculate the new volume.

6. The volume of a fixed mass of gas is 1400 cm^3 at 27 ^{o}C.

    Calculate the volume of gas at 127 ^{o}C if the gas pressure doubles.

7. The volume of a fixed mass of gas is 12 m^3 at 127 ^{o}C.

    Calculate the volume of gas at 27 ^{o}C if the pressure drops to one third of its original value.

8. A gas bubble has a volume of 10 cm^3. The pressure of the gas in the bubble is 1 x 10^5 Pa and the temperature is 7 ^{o}C.

    If the pressure is reduced to 5 x 10^4 Pa and its volume increases to 25 cm^3, calculate the new temperature of the gas, in degrees celsius.

9. The pressure of a fixed mass of gas is doubled and its kelvin temperature is also doubled.

    What happens to the volume of gas after these changes?
    Give your answer as a fraction of the original volume.

10. The pressure of a fixed mass of gas is 200 kPa. The kelvin temperature of the gas trebles and its volume doubles.

    Calculate the new pressure of the gas.

11. During an experiment involving a fixed mass of gas, the pressure doubles and the volume is trebled.

    How does the final kelvin temperature of the gas compare with the original kelvin temperature?

Exercise 3.7   Pressure in Liquids

1. The pressure at a depth of 0.5 m in a particular liquid is 3750 Pa above atmospheric pressure.

    At what depth would the pressure rise to 17.5 kPa above atmospheric pressure?

2. The pressure at a certain depth of fresh water is 20 kPa above atmospheric pressure.

    What would the pressure be at the same depth in another liquid with a density of 1.25 times that of water?

3. A liquid container has an irregular shape as shown. It contains the same liquid throughout.

    Which column of liquid produces the greatest pressure at the bottom?

4. A water filled manometer is connected to a gas supply as shown. A height difference of 35 cm is produced. Atmospheric pressure is 1 x 10^5 Pa.

    a) Calculate the pressure of the gas supply.
    b) Calculate the height difference which would be produced if the same supply was attached to a mercury filled manometer.
        (Take the density of water to be 1000 kg m^{-3} and the density of mercury to be 13 600 kg m^{-3}.)

    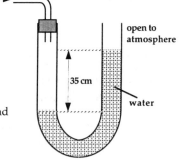

5. A pressure sensor is lowered into a large beaker of liquid as shown.

    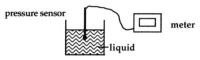

    The sensor is set to read zero in the air above the beaker.

    Sketch a graph to show how the pressure varies against depth as the sensor is lowered into the liquid.

6. Both ends of the tube shown are sealed. The density of the liquid in the tube is 820 kg m⁻³.

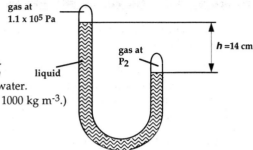

gas at 1.1 x 10⁵ Pa

gas at P₂

liquid

h =14 cm

a) Calculate the pressure P_2 of the gas in the lower part of the tube.
b) Calculate the height difference h if the same tube was filled with water.
(Take the density of water to be 1000 kg m⁻³.)

7. Pressure can be measured in centimetres of mercury. Using this unit, 76 cm of mercury is equivalent to a pressure of 100 kPa. Air is trapped above a column of mercury in a sealed tube as shown. The atmospheric pressure of the air outside the tube is equivalent to 76 cm of mercury.

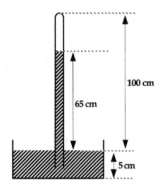

100 cm

65 cm

5 cm

a) What is the pressure of the air trapped at the top of the tube, in centimetres of mercury?
b) What would this pressure be in pascals?
c) The mercury is replaced with water and the tube is replaced with a much longer tube. Calculate the equivalent height of the column of water.
(Take the density of water to be 1000 kg m⁻³.)

8. A mercury filled manometer is connected to a vessel containing gas as shown. The atmospheric pressure of the air outside the vessel is equivalent to 76 cm of mercury.

Calculate the pressure of the gas in the vessel, in centimetres of mercury.

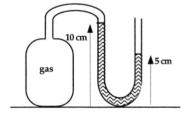

10 cm

5 cm

gas

Exercise 3.8   Buoyancy and Flotation

1. Explain why an object weighs less when suspended in water than it does when suspended in air.

2. An object has an apparent loss of weight of 0.8 N in water.
    What will be the apparent loss of weight in mercury?
    (Take the density of water to be 1×10^3 kg m^{-3} and the density of mercury to be 13.6×10^3 kg m^{-3}.)

3. A boat floats at a depth of 2.5 m in fresh water (density 1000 kg m^{-3}).
    At what depth will it float if the boat moved into sea water (density 1030 kg m^{-3})?

4. A piece of material of dimensions of 25 cm x 40 cm x 100 cm floats as shown 1.75 m below the surface of a liquid of density 1200 kg m^{-3}.

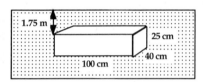

    a) Calculate the pressure on the top surface of the object.
    b) Calculate the pressure on the bottom surface of the object.
    c) Calculate the force on the top surface of the object.
    d) Calculate the force on the bottom surface of the object.
    e) Calculate the buoyancy force on the object.
    f) Calculate the density of the material of the block.

5. Explain why it is impossible to find the mass of air in a balloon by weighing the balloon initially and then weighing the inflated balloon.

6. Explain why a sunken ship can be raised by filling it with polystyrene balls.

7. **a)** How does the upthrust of the water vary when a ship sails up river from the sea into increasingly fresh water?
    b) What happens to the depth to which the ship's hull sinks below the water?

8. What would be the upthrust of water on a 55 kg swimmer floating in a pool at a base on Mars in the 22nd century?
    (gravitational field strength on Mars = 3.8 N kg^{-1})

9. A 57 kg female astronaut is floating in a swimming pool on the Moon where the gravitational field strength is 1.7 N kg^{-1}.
    Calculate the upthrust exerted on her body by the water in the swimming pool.

10. A brick of mass 3.5 kg is supported underwater by a newton balance which reads 21 N.
    What is the buoyancy force on the brick?

11. Explain why a piece of iron (density 870 kg m^{-3}) will float in a beaker of mercury (density 13 600 kg m^{-3}).

12. A 5 kg brick is supported in a basin of water (density 1000 kg m^{-3}) by a spring balance which reads 44 N.

    a) Calculate the buoyancy force acting on the brick.

    b) i) The brick is now placed in a basin of glycerol (density 1260 kg m^{-3}). How will the reading on the spring balance compare with the reading in water. Explain your answer.

       ii) As the brick is lowered deeper into the glycerol, what will happen to the reading on the spring balance? Explain your answer.

13. Test tubes containing different masses float in water as shown.

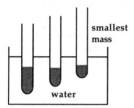

    a) What conclusion can be drawn from this experiment?

    b) Describe a similar experiment which could be performed to show the effect of density on the depth at which a test tube would float.

    c) Explain why the pressure at a fixed depth varies with the density of the liquid.

14. A hot air balloon is tethered to the ground on a windless day. The envelope of the balloon contains 1200 m^3 of hot air of density 0.8 kg m^{-3}. The mass of the balloon not including the hot air is 400 kg. The balloon experiences an upthrust of 15 600 N.

    a) What is the mass of the hot air in the balloon?

    b) Calculate the tension in the rope holding the balloon to the ground.

    c) Explain why the balloon would rise if it were not tethered.

    d) Calculate the acceleration of the balloon when the tethering rope is released.

15. A submarine has a total mass of 7.8 x 10^6 kg. The submarine floats at a depth of 50 m in seawater of density 1030 kg m^{-3}.

    a) i) Calculate the weight of the submarine.

       ii) State the upthrust on the submarine.

    b) The submarine pumps seawater out of its ballast tanks in order to ascend with an acceleration of 0.1 m s^{-2}. What volume of seawater is pumped out?

    c) What effect would there be on the submarine, if it moved into fresh water after pumping out its ballast tanks?

Exercise 3.9   Mixed Problems

1. A diver's cylinder with a capacity of 0.06 m³ has 0.4 m³ of air at atmospheric pressure (density 1.44 kg m⁻³) compressed into it.
    a) What is the pressure inside the gas cylinder when filled? State the assumption which is made.
    b) What is the density of the air in the cylinder?
    c) i)   What is the pressure 10 m under the water? (Take the density of water to be 1000 kg m⁻³.)
       ii) If the diver is 10 m under the water, what volume of air is available for her?
       iii) If she uses 25 cm³ of air per second how long could she remain under the water?

2. A plastic container is placed on a balance and then extra air is pumped into the container using a foot pump. This extra air is then released into a measuring cylinder as shown and its volume measured. The following measurements are recorded.

    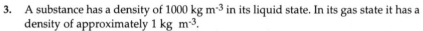

Mass of container full of air	=	362.00 g
Mass of container with extra air	=	363.86 g
Volume of air released	=	1687.00 cm³

    What value do these results give for the density of air, in kilograms per cubic metre?

3. A substance has a density of 1000 kg m⁻³ in its liquid state. In its gas state it has a density of approximately 1 kg m⁻³.

    Show that these figures are consistent with the average molecular separation in a gas being about ten time that in a liquid.

4. The graph shows how the force exerted by one molecule, positioned at O, on a similar molecule varies with the distance the molecules are apart.

    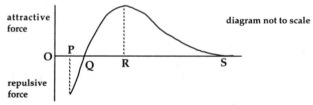

    State the point (P, Q, R or S) which gives the approximate separation between the molecules in
    a) the solid state,
    b) the gaseous state.

5. A flat-bottomed can of weight 5 N floats with its bottom 0.10 m below the surface of a liquid of density 1.0 x 10³ kg m⁻³.

    If it is to float at the same depth in a liquid of density 1.2 x 10³ kg m⁻³, how must the weight of the can be adjusted?

6. The handle of a bicycle pump is pulled out filling the pump with air. If the outlet is then blocked and the handle pushed in suddenly, the pressure of the enclosed air increases and so does its temperature.

   Explain both of these changes in terms of the behaviour of the molecules of air in the pump.

7. A suction hook is pressed against a smooth wall and is held in place by atmospheric pressure.

   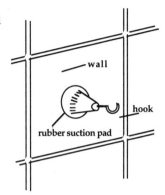

   a) Calculate the maximum force required to pull the hook off the wall if the diameter of the circular pad in contact with the wall is 0.030 m and the atmospheric pressure is 1.0×10^5 Pa.
   b) Suggest **two** reasons why this maximum force, measured by an experiment, would be likely to be less than the value you have calculated in part **a)**.

8. The porous pot used in the experiment shown is made of unglazed porcelain. Gas molecules can diffuse through this material.

   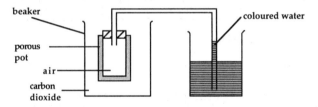

   a) The beaker is filled with carbon dioxide.
      Explain fully why, after a short time, the coloured water rises up the tube.
   b) After a few minutes the beaker containing the carbon dioxide is removed. State and explain what will then happen.

9. The graph shows how the pressure of a fixed mass of gas at 27 °C varies with volume from **A** to **B** to **C**. Both pressure and volume are in arbitrary units.

   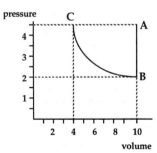

   a) Which gas law applies over **AB**?
   b) Which gas law applies over **BC**?
   c) What temperature corresponds to position **B**?

Resistors in Circuits

Exercise 4.1   Resistors

1. The diagram shows part of an electrical circuit.
    What is the resistance between **X** and **Y**?

    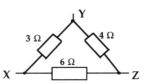

2. Three resistors are connected as shown.

    Calculate the total resistance between
    a) **XY**,
    b) **XZ**,
    c) **YZ**.

    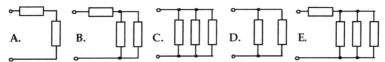

3. All the resistors in the diagrams shown have the same resistance.

    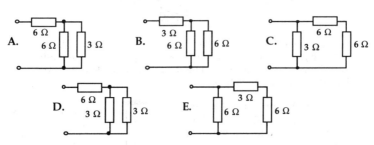

    Identify the arrangement which has
    a) the least resistance,
    b) the greatest resistance.

4.

    A. 6 Ω 6 Ω 3 Ω
    B. 3 Ω 6 Ω 6 Ω
    C. 6 Ω 3 Ω 6 Ω
    D. 6 Ω 3 Ω 3 Ω
    E. 3 Ω 6 Ω 6 Ω

    Identify the arrangement which has
    a) the least resistance,
    b) the greatest resistance.

5. Three different resistors are available. Their values are 4 Ω, 6 Ω and 12 Ω.

    Describe how two, or all three, of the resistors might be combined to give each of the
    following resistances.
    a) 10 Ω
    b) 3 Ω
    c) 8 Ω

6. In the following circuit, the sliding contact of the rheostat moves from **X** to **Y**.

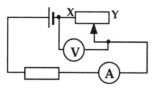

a) Explain whether the ammeter reading increases, decreases or stay constant.
b) Explain whether the voltmeter reading increases, decreases or stay constant.

7. The overhead cables used in a 132 kV grid system consist of 7 strands of steel wire and 30 strands of aluminium wire. The 7 strands of steel have a **combined** resistance of 3.0 ohms per kilometre and the 30 strands of aluminium have a **combined** resistance of 0.17 ohms per kilometre.

a) Show that the resistance of the cable is 0.16 ohms per kilometre.
b) Why should steel wire be used in the cable even though it has a much higher resistance than aluminium?
c) A typical current in the cable is 400 A.
Calculate the power loss per kilometre of cable for this current.

8. The resistance of a length of bare uniform resistance wire is 30 Ω. The length of wire is folded into the shape of a square and the ends soldered together as shown.

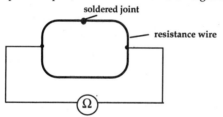

soldered joint

resistance wire

What value of resistance would the ohmmeter read if it is connected as shown at the mid-points of opposite sides of the square?
(You may ignore the resistance of the ohmmeter leads.)

9. Some resistors are constructed by depositing a thin film of conducting material on top of an insulating base. The resistance depends on the breadth of the conducting film. The results show the resistance for various breadths of film of the same length and thickness.

Breadth/mm	150	87	67	60	55
Resistance/Ω	80	140	180	200	220

Find the relationship between the resistance and the breadth of the conducting film. You must use all the data and show your working.

Exercise 4.2   Potential Dividers

1. Two potential dividers **PQ** are set up as shown.

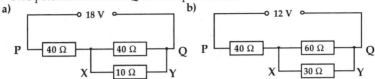

a)   18 V

P   40 Ω   40 Ω   Q

X   10 Ω   Y

b)   12 V

P   40 Ω   60 Ω   Q

X   30 Ω   Y

In each case, what is the potential difference across the resistor **XY**?

2. Four resistors each of value 8 Ω are connected across a 60 V supply of negligible internal resistance as shown.

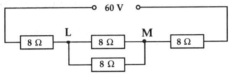

60 V

8 Ω   L   8 Ω   M   8 Ω

8 Ω

Find the p.d. across **LM**.

3. A 20 V supply is connected to a set of resistors in series as shown.

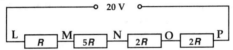

20 V

L   R   M   5R   N   2R   O   2R   P

Between which two points would a voltmeter read 8 V?

4. The circuit shows resistors connected as a potential divider.

   Calculate the reading on the voltmeter
   a) when the switch **S** is open,
   b) when the switch **S** is closed.

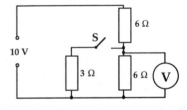

10 V   S   6 Ω   3 Ω   6 Ω   V

5. A potential divider is shown in the diagram.
   a) Calculate the p.d. between **X** and **Y**.
   b) A motor of resistance 50 Ω is connected across the terminals **X** and **Y**.
      i) Calculate the p.d. across the motor.
      ii) State the relationship between power, voltage and resistance.
      iii) Calculate the power supplied to this motor.

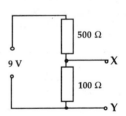

9 V   500 Ω   X   100 Ω   Y

6. In the potential divider circuit shown, the variable resistor allows the potential difference between **X** and **Y** to be varied.

For the values given, what is the maximum potential difference which can be obtained across **XY**?

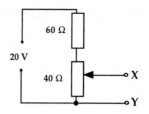

7. In the following circuit, the p.d. across the 16 Ω resistor is 40 V when switch **S** is **open**.

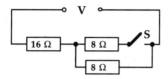

a) What is the voltage of the supply?
b) What is the p.d. across the 16 Ω resistor when the switch **S** is **closed**?

8. The circuit shown is used to provide output voltages of 3.0 V and 6.0 V from a 9.0 V battery of negligible internal resistance.

a) If the resistance of **Q** is 100 Ω, find the resistance of **P**.
b) A 6 V, 0.060 A lamp is now connected across resistor **Q** .
   Calculate the resistance of the lamp and hence explain why the lamp does not operate at its normal brightness.
c) What value of resistor should be used at **P** in order that the bulb does work at its correct brightness?

9. You are given a fixed 10 V d.c. supply, a 1.5 kΩ resistor and a 1.0 kΩ variable resistor.

a) Draw a circuit diagram which shows how you would connect these components to supply a variable voltage of up to 4.0 V.
   Label the output terminals in your diagram.
b) When the variable supply is set at 4 V, a 1 kΩ resistor is now connected across the output terminals.
   i)   Explain why the voltage across the terminals is now less than 4 V.
   ii) Calculate the new voltage across the terminals.

Exercise 4.3 Electrical Energy and Power

1. For each of the circuits, calculate the total power developed.

   a)   b)

   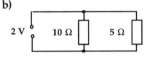

2. How much electrical energy is converted in the two bulbs in 16 s?

   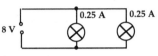

3. The ammeter in the circuit shown registers 2 A.

   How much energy is converted to heat in the resistor in 1 minute?

   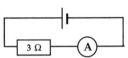

4. An immersion heater is connected to a constant voltage supply. 2000 J of energy is required to supply a current of 2 A for 4 s through the immersion heater.

   Calculate the potential difference, in volts, between the ends of the heater.

5. The diagram shows three identical light bulbs connected to a constant 12 V d.c. supply. Each bulb has a resistance of 72 Ω when operating at normal brightness. The ammeter registers 0.5 A and has negligible resistance.

   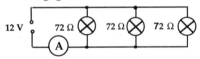

   A break occurs in the filament of one of the bulbs.

   a) Calculate the new reading on the ammeter.
   b) State what happens to the brightness of the other two bulbs.

6. An electrical heater has a power of 500 Ω when operated at 250 V.

   If it were used on a 125 V supply, what would be its electrical power? (Assume that its resistance remains the same.)

7. In the circuit shown, the power drawn from the supply, which has negligible internal resistance, is 30 Ω when the switch **S** is closed.

   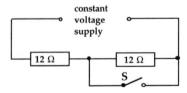

   What power is delivered to the circuit by the supply when the switch is open?

8. When a single resistor **R** is connected, 400 Ω is drawn from the supply.

a) 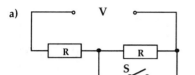   b)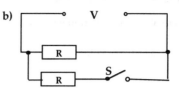

In each of the above circuits, calculate the power drawn from the same supply
   i)   when **S** is open,
   ii) when **S** is closed.
(Assume all the resistors are identical and the supply has negligible internal resistance.)

9. The power transferred to the resistor in circuit **1** is 100 W.

Circuit 1 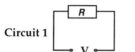   Circuit 2

What is the power transferred to the resistor in circuit **2**?

10. The resistance of one wire, **A**, is three times as great as that of another wire, **B**.

   a) How does the power developed in the two wires compare when they are connected **in parallel** across the same source of supply?
   b) How does the power developed in the two wires compare when they are connected **in series** across the same source of supply?

11. Three 12 V, 24 W bulbs are connected as shown.

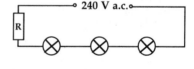

   a) Calculate the current in each bulb when operating at its correct power.
   b) Calculate the resistance of resistor **R** which allows the three bulbs to be run at their correct power.
   c) What fraction of the input power is used by the bulbs?
   d) Give the reason why the power used by the bulbs is less than the input power.
   e) Suggest another way of providing the correct voltage for the three bulbs.

12. A mains light bulb is 16% efficient. The current through the bulb is 0.261 A.

   a) What is the power of the bulb?
   b) How much energy is produced in the form of light in 5 minutes?
   c) How much energy is produced in the form of heat in 5 minutes?

13. In the diagram plate **A** is at a potential of 100 V and plate **B** is at a potential of 300 V. A charge of 5 C was passed from **A** to **B**.

What was the energy, in joules, required for this?

Exercise 4.4   Circuits

1. In the circuit shown the ammeter reads 2 A.

    Calculate the supply voltage.

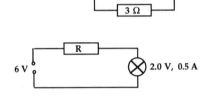

2. The current delivered by the power supply in the circuit shown is 3 A.

    Assuming the power supply has negligible internal resistance, find the resistance of resistor **R**.

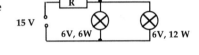

3. A 2.0 V, 0.5 A bulb is connected to a 6 V d.c. supply as shown. The supply has negligible internal resistance.

    If the bulb is to operate at its correct rating, calculate the resistance of resistor **R**.

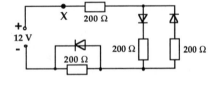

4. The two bulbs in the circuit shown operate at their correct ratings.

    Calculate the resistance of resistor **R**. (Assume the power supply has negligible internal resistance.)

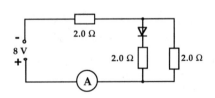

5. In the circuit shown, the diodes have negligible forward resistance and infinite reverse resistance.

    What is the current in the circuit at point **X**?

6. The circuit shown includes a diode which has negligible forward resistance and infinite reverse resistance.

    Calculate the reading on the ammeter
    a) with the diode as shown,
    b) if the diode is reversed.

Exercise 4.5   E.m.f. and Internal Resistance

1. A battery of e.m.f. 12 V and internal
    resistance 1 Ω is connected across a
    2 Ω resistor, as shown in the circuit.

    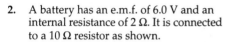

    a) Calculate the current flowing in the circuit.
    b) Calculate the terminal potential difference
       (t.p.d.) across the battery.
    c) What is the value of the 'lost volts'?

2. A battery has an e.m.f. of 6.0 V and an
    internal resistance of 2 Ω. It is connected
    to a 10 Ω resistor as shown.

    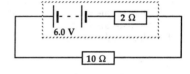

    a) Calculate the p.d. across the 10 Ω resistor.
    b) The 10 Ω resistor is removed and the
       battery is short circuited by connecting a
       thick copper wire across the terminals.
       Calculate the short circuit current.

3. A battery has an e.m.f. of 12 V and an
    internal resistance of 2.0 Ω. It is connected
    to a 4 Ω resistor in the following circuit.

    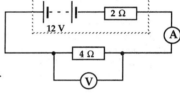

    a) Calculate the reading on
       i)   the ammeter,
       ii) the voltmeter.
    b) The 4 Ω resistor is replaced by a 2 Ω resistor.
       Calculate the new reading on
       i)   the ammeter,
       ii) the voltmeter.

4. A battery of e.m.f. 5.0 V is connected to a 10 Ω resistor and a current of 400 mA flows
    through the resistor.

    Calculate the internal resistance of the battery.

5. Three cells each of e.m.f. 2 V, and an internal resistance of 1 Ω are connected in series,
    to form a battery. The battery is connected across a 3 Ω resistor.

    Calculate the current in the circuit.

6. A voltmeter connected across a cell reads 1.5 V. The reading on the voltmeter drops to
    1.0 V when the cell is connected to a 20 Ω resistor.

    Find the internal resistance of the cell.

7. The voltmeter and ammeter readings in the circuit shown are taken at various settings of the variable resistor and the graph plotted.

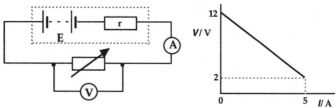

a) What is the e.m.f. of the battery?
b) Calculate the internal resistance of the battery.
c) Calculate the short circuit current for the battery.
d) Calculate the power produced in the variable resistor when it is set at 4 Ω.

8. A radio battery consists of six identical 1.5 V cells in series. When the terminals of the battery are connected by a short piece of thick copper wire, the current is 0.5 A.

Find the internal resistance of **each** cell.

9. a) State what is meant by the e.m.f. of a battery.
b) Use the information from the graph shown to find
   i) the e.m.f. of the battery,
   ii) the internal resistance of the battery.
c) Explain why the reading on a voltmeter placed across the battery decreases as the current drawn from the battery increases.

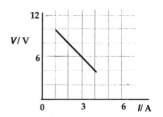

10. A battery is connected to a calibrated variable resistor **R** and an ammeter as shown and a graph plotted of **R** against 1/*I*.

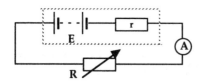

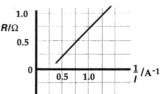

a) For this circuit derive the expression:

$$R = \frac{E}{I} - r$$

b) Explain why the graph of **R** against 1/*I* is drawn.
c) Use the graph to find the e.m.f. of the battery, the internal resistance and the short circuit current.

11. A heater of resistance 0.32 Ω is connected to a power supply of e.m.f. 2.0 V and internal resistance **r**. The power output of the **heater** is 8.0 W.
a) i) Calculate the current in the heater.
   ii) Calculate the p.d. across the heater.
b) Calculate the internal resistance **r** of the power supply.
c) Another identical heater is connected in parallel with the original heater. The rest of the circuit is unaltered. Calculate the total power output of the two heaters.

Exercise 4.6   Wheatstone Bridges

1. In the circuits shown the current in the milliammeter is zero.
   Calculate each of the resistances **X**, **Y** and **Z**.

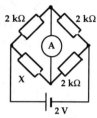
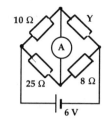
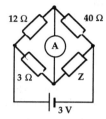

2. Bulb **X** in the circuit shown has a
   rating 12 V, 24 W and is operating
   at its correct rating.

   If the Wheatstone Bridge is balanced
   find the resistance of resistor **R**.

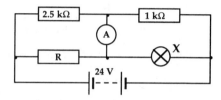

3. In the Wheatstone bridge circuit
   shown, there is a small potential
   difference on the voltmeter **V**.

   a) State what change could be made
   to resistor **A** in order to balance
   the bridge.
   b) Repeat for each of the other resistors
   B, **C** and **D**.

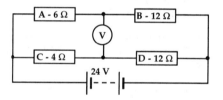

4. In the bridge circuit shown the
   variable resistor **R** is adjusted so
   that the bridge is balanced at 18 °C.
   The thermistor is now placed in a
   beaker containing melting ice.

   a) How does the resistance of the
   thermistor vary when it is placed
   in the melting ice?
   b) In order to rebalance the bridge, state the changes which could be made to
   i)   **P** (all other resistors unchanged),
   ii)   **Q** (all other resistors unchanged).

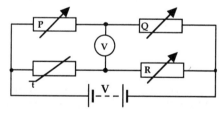

5. a) State the reading on the voltmeter in the circuit shown.
   b) The 4 kΩ resistor is replaced by a variable resistor which is increased gradually from 3950 Ω to 4050 Ω. Sketch the graph of resistance against voltmeter reading. (Numerical values are only required on the resistance axis.)

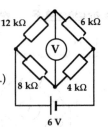

6. The diagram shows a balanced Wheatstone bridge circuit.

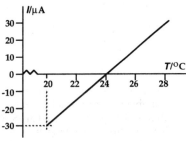

   a) Explain what is meant by a balanced Wheatstone bridge.
   b) After a period of use the p.d. across the battery in the circuit decreases to half its original value. What effect does this have on the reading on the galvanometer? Justify your answer.
   c) In practice, why is it necessary to protect the galvanometer? Describe a suitable method of doing this.
   d) Calculate the value of resistor S if P = 720 ± 10 Ω, Q = 320 ± 10 Ω, and R = 360 ± 25 Ω. Include an absolute uncertainty in your answer.

7. In the circuit shown R_1 is a thermistor and R_2 is set at 760 Ω. The temperature of R_1 changes from 20 °C to 28 °C and a graph of ammeter current against temperature is drawn.

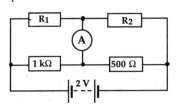

   a) What is the temperature when the bridge is balanced?
   b) Calculate the resistance of the temperature sensing resistor when the circuit is balanced.
   c) The resistance of R_1 increases with temperature. Copy the above graph and on the same axes sketch the graph which would be obtained if R_2 is set at a slightly greater resistance and the temperature of R_1 again changes from 20 °C to 28 °C.

Exercise 4.7   Electric Fields

(charge on the electron, e, = -1.6 x 10^{-19} C;   mass of the electron, m_e, = 9.11 x 10^{-31} kg)

1. Explain what happens to a charged particle placed in an electric field.

2. Copy and sketch the electric field round each of the following.
    a) Isolated positive charge
    b) Isolated negative charge

    c) Parallel plates
    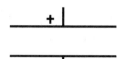

    d) Pair of charged spheres

3. Calculate the energy dissipated
    when one coulomb of charge passes
    through
    a) the 50 Ω resistor,
    b) the 100 Ω resistor.

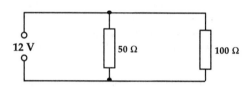

4. The electric field within the electron gun of a oscilloscope accelerates an electron from rest. There is a potential difference of 20 kV between the cathode and the final anode.
    Calculate the velocity of the electron as it passes the anode.

5. In the electric field within the electron gun of a television tube, an electron is accelerated from rest by a potential difference of 25 kV between the cathode and the final anode.
    Calculate the velocity of the electron as it passes the anode.

6. A potential difference of 20 V exists between the terminals of an electric motor.
    What does this mean?
    (i.e. explain in terms of energy and charge what a potential difference of 20 V means.)

7. The electrons in an oscilloscope are accelerated from cathode to anode by a potential difference of 2000 V.
    If the p.d. is increased to 8000 V, state the effect this would have on
    a) the kinetic energy of the electrons on arriving at the screen,
    b) the velocity of the electrons on arriving at the screen.

8. A charged particle is fired between a pair of parallel plates as shown.

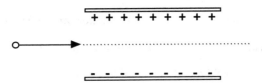

a) Copy the diagram and complete the path of the electron.
b) On leaving the plate the electron has been deflected by 1 unit. An oppositely charged particle, which has double the charge and the same mass as the first, is fired with the same velocity between the plates.
    Add the path of this particle to your diagram, and state by how many units it is deflected.
c) The particle in part b) has a mass 4 times greater than before and still has double the charge and the same velocity.
    Sketch its trajectory and state by how many units it is deflected.

9. Define the volt.

10. In the arrangement shown, 2 C of positive charge is moved from plate S, which is at a potential of 250 V, to plate T, which is at a potential of 750 V.

    How much energy is required to move this charge from plate S to plate T?

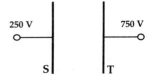

11. A particle accelerator increases the speed of protons by accelerating them between a pair of parallel metal plates, A and B, connected to a power supply as shown.

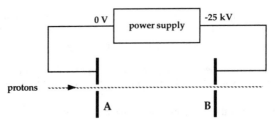

The potential difference between A and B is 25 kV.

a) Show that the kinetic energy gained by a proton between plates A and B is 4.5×10^{-15} J.
b) The kinetic energy of a proton at plate A is 1.3×10^{-16} J.
    Calculate the velocity of the proton on reaching plate B.
    (mass of the proton, $m_p, = 1.67 \times 10^{-27}$ kg)

Analogue Electronics

Exercise 5.1   Inverting Mode

The questions all refer to the following diagram of an op-amp in inverting mode.
The supply voltage for the op-amp is ±15 V.

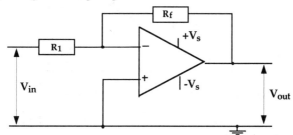

1. For each of the following, state the voltage gain.
    a) V_{in} = 600 μV V_{out} = -750 mV
    b) R_1 = 220 kΩ R_f = 10 MΩ

2. For each of the following, find the output voltage.
    a) R_1 = 10 kΩ R_f = 100 kΩ V_{in} = 20 mV
    b) R_1 = 100 kΩ R_f = 1 MΩ V_{in} = 0.6 V
    c) R_1 = 50 kΩ R_f = 150 kΩ V_{in} = -4.3 mV
    d) R_1 = 40 kΩ R_f = 1 MΩ V_{in} = 17 mV

3. For each of the following, find the input voltage.
    a) R_1 = 10 kΩ R_f = 150 kΩ V_{out} = -5 V
    b) R_1 = 100 kΩ R_f = 1 MΩ V_{out} = -11.4 V
    c) R_1 = 100 kΩ R_f = 750 kΩ V_{out} = 870 mV
    d) R_1 = 1 MΩ R_f = 20 kΩ V_{out} = - 20 mV

4. For each of the following, find the value of the feedback resistor.
    a) R_1 = 10 kΩ V_{in} = 150 mV V_{out} = -1.5 V
    b) R_1 = 50 kΩ V_{in} = -625 mV V_{out} = 12.5 V
    c) R_1 = 75 kΩ V_{in} = 525 μV V_{out} = -84 mV
    d) R_1 = 1 MΩ V_{in} = 8 V V_{out} = - 100 mV

5. For each of the following, find the value of the input resistor.
    a) R_f = 100 kΩ V_{in} = 1.3 V V_{out} = -4.55 V
    b) R_f = 10 MΩ V_{in} = 367 mV V_{out} = -7.8 V
    c) R_f = 2.2 MΩ V_{in} = 825 μV V_{out} = -0.2 V
    d) R_f = 4.7 MΩ V_{in} = 94 mV V_{out} = -13.39 V

Exercise 5.2   Inverting Mode, Saturation

The questions all refer to the following diagram of an op-amp in inverting mode.

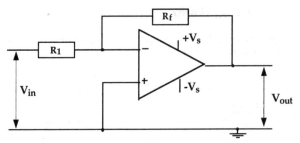

1.   If the supply voltage is ±15 V, what is the maximum value of V_{out}?

2.   If R_1 = 10 kΩ and R_f = 100 kΩ, find the output voltage for each of the following values of V_{in}. The supply voltage is ± 15 V.

   a) V_{in} = 150 mV
   b) V_{in} = 850 mV
   c) V_{in} = 2.50 V

3.   If R_1 = 47 kΩ and R_f = 1 MΩ, find the output voltage for each of the following values of V_{in}. The supply voltage is ± 12 V.

   a) V_{in} = 2500 μV
   b) V_{in} = 0.510 V
   c) V_{in} = 0.98 V

4.   If the supply voltage is ±15 V, what value of R_f will produce saturation in each of the following cases?

   a) R_1 = 100 kΩ and V_{in} = 2.5 V
   b) R_1 = 560 kΩ and V_{in} = 725 mV
   c) R_1 = 47 kΩ and V_{in} = 1.6 V

5.   If the supply voltage is ±12 V, what value of R_1 will produce saturation in each of the following cases?

   a) R_f = 10 MΩ and V_{in} = 1.2 V
   b) R_f = 2.2 MΩ and V_{in} = 900 mV
   c) R_f = 5600 kΩ and V_{in} = 0.05 V

Exercise 5.3   Inverting Mode, Analogue Inputs

The questions all refer to the following diagram of an op-amp in inverting mode. The supply voltage is ± 15 V.

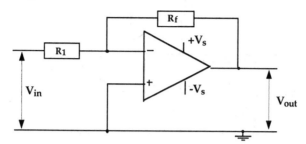

1. The input signal to the op-amp is shown.

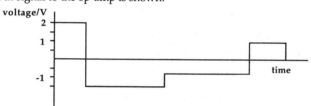

Sketch the input signal and underneath draw the output signal in each case. (Numerical values are required on the voltage axis.)

a) R_1 = 50 kΩ and R_f = 200 kΩ
b) R_1 = 10 kΩ and R_f = 100 kΩ

2. The input signal to the op-amp is shown.

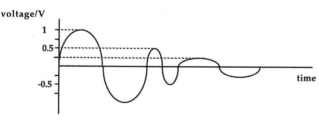

Sketch the input signal and underneath draw the output signal in each case. (Numerical values are required on the voltage axis.)

a) R_1 = 100 kΩ and R_f = 1 MΩ
b) R_1 = 25 kΩ and R_f = 1 MΩ

Exercise 5.4   Differential Mode

The questions all refer to the following diagram of an op-amp in differential mode. The supply voltage for the op-amp is ±15 V.

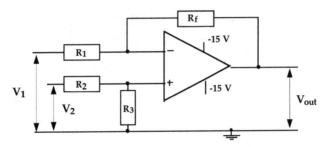

1. What is the main use of an op-amp connected in this mode?

2. Calculate the value of R_3 for each of the following.

   a) R_1 = 100 kΩ R_f = 1 MΩ R_2 = 10 kΩ
   b) R_1 = 50 kΩ R_f = 330 kΩ R_2 = 40 kΩ

3. Calculate the output voltage for each of the following.

   a) R_1 = 100 kΩ R_f = 1 MΩ V_1 = 0.5 V V_2 = 0.3 V
   b) R_1 = 100 kΩ R_f = 1 MΩ V_1 = -0.5 V V_2 = 0.3 V
   c) R_1 = 40 kΩ R_f = 100 kΩ V_1 = 600 mV V_2 = -1.3 V
   d) R_1 = 150 kΩ R_f = 2.2 MΩ V_1 = 40 µV V_2 = 6 mV
   e) R_1 = 25 kΩ R_f = 1 MΩ V_1 = 580 mV V_2 = 920 mV

4. Calculate the input voltage V_1 if:
   R_1 = 10 kΩ R_f = 560 kΩ V_2 = 0.6 V and V_{out} = - 180 mV

5. Calculate the input voltage V_2 if:
   R_1 = 470 kΩ R_f = 220 kΩ V_2 = 1.73 V and V_{out} = 900 mV

6. Calculate the maximum and minimum output voltages if R_f is a variable resistor ranging from 500 kΩ to 2500 kΩ and:
   R_1 = 100 kΩ V_1 = 4.5 V and V_2 = 3.6 V

Exercise 5.5   Differential Mode, Analogue Inputs

The questions all refer to the following diagram of an op-amp in differential mode. The supply voltage for the op-amp is ±15 V.

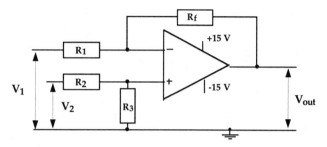

1. The input signals to the op-amp are shown.

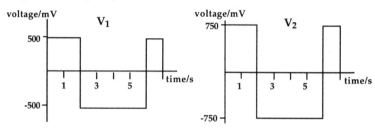

Sketch the output signal in each case.
(Numerical values are required on both axes.)

a) $R_1 = 50\ k\Omega$ and $R_f = 200\ k\Omega$
b) $R_1 = 1\ M\Omega$ and $R_f = 100\ k\Omega$

2. The input signals to the op-amp are shown.

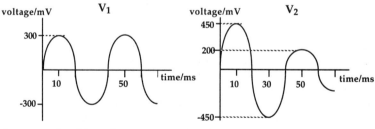

Sketch the output signal in each case.
(Numerical values are required on both axes.)

a) $R_1 = 200\ k\Omega$ and $R_f = 1\ M\Omega$
b) $R_1 = 2200\ k\Omega$ and $R_f = 4.7\ M\Omega$

Exercise 5.6   Differential Mode, Monitoring Circuits

1. A Wheatstone bridge containing a light dependent resistor is connected to an op-amp as shown.

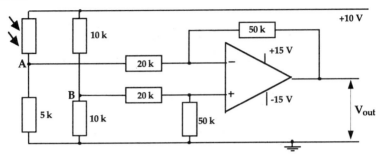

a) What is the voltage at point **B**?
b) In bright light the resistance of the LDR is 600 Ω.
    i)   Calculate the potential at point **A**.
    ii) Calculate the output voltage, V_{out}.
c) In the dark the resistance of the LDR is 1.5 kΩ.
    i)   Calculate the potential at point **A**.
    ii) Calculate the new output voltage, V_{out}.

2. A Wheatstone bridge containing a thermistor is connected to an op-amp as shown.

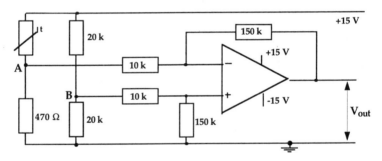

a) What is the voltage at point **B**?
b) When cold the resistance of the thermistor is 500 Ω.
    i)   Calculate the potential at point **A**.
    ii) Calculate the output voltage, V_{out}.
c) When warm the resistance of the thermistor is 450 Ω.
    i)   Calculate the potential at point **A**.
    ii) Calculate the output voltage, V_{out}.

Exercise 5.7 Control Circuits

1. The circuit shown is used to warn a photographer when a flash is required.

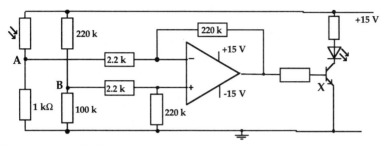

a) In what mode is the op-amp working?
b) At a certain light intensity the output from the op-amp is zero.
   What is the resistance of the LDR under these conditions?
c) Explain what happens when the light intensity on the LDR starts to decrease and
   how the circuit would indicate that a flash is required.
d) i) What is component **X**?
   ii) State the purpose of component **X**.
e) If the output voltage from the op-amp is 0.95 V, calculate the potential difference
   between points **A** and **B** in the diagram.

2. The following is part of a circuit which can be used to close windows when it starts
   raining. Component **R** is a moisture sensitive resistor whose resistance decreases from
   100 kΩ to 10 kΩ when rain falls on it.

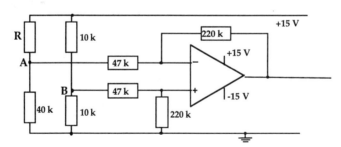

a) Calculate the voltage at point **B**.
b) i) Calculate the voltage at point **A** when **R** is dry.
   ii) Calculate the output voltage from the op-amp when **R** is dry.
c) i) Calculate the voltage at point **A** when **R** is wet.
   ii) Calculate the output voltage from the op-amp when **R** is wet.
d) The next stage in the circuit turns on a motor in the wet.
   Copy the above circuit and add the following components to show how this could
   be done.

Exercise 5.8   Mixed Problems

1   a) State **two** properties an ideal op-amp should have.
    b) Why are each of these properties important?

2.

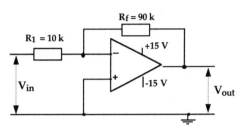

a) What is the purpose of R_f?
b) Calculate the output voltage for an input voltage of +0.20 V.
c) Redraw the circuit, using the same components, to show how an input of -18 V
   can be reduced to 2 V.

3.

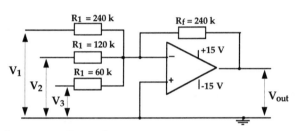

a) Calculate the output voltage when:
   $V_1 = 1$ V $V_2 = 1$ V   and $V_3 = 0$ V
b) If the inputs can be set at either 0 or 1, what range of output voltages are available?
c) What might this circuit be used for?
d) How could the range of values for the output voltage be extended?

4.   The diagram shows a small high frequency signal of amplitude 5 mV, superimposed
     on a sine wave of frequency 50 Hz and amplitude 1.2 V.

Another 50 Hz sine wave of variable amplitude is available from a signal generator.
A technician wishes to remove the sine wave and show only the high frequency signal.

a) Draw a circuit which would allow the technician to show just the high frequency
   signal.
b) Explain how this circuit works.
c) Suggest suitable values of resistors which would allow the technician to amplify the
   small signal to give an amplitude of ±10 V.

5. A 2-stage amplifier is shown.

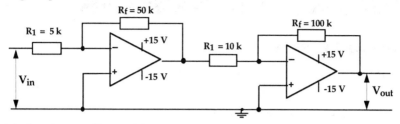

a) Calculate the overall gain of the circuit.
b) If the input signal is 10 mV, calculate the output voltage.
c) What is the maximum input signal which will not produce saturation in the second amplifier?

6. a) A solar cell is used to compare the output of lamps. Initially the lamp is off.

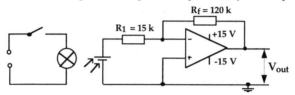

When set up near a window, there is an output voltage of -1.75 V.
i) Explain why the output voltage is **not** zero.
ii) Calculate the solar cell voltage.
b) The circuit is now altered as shown.

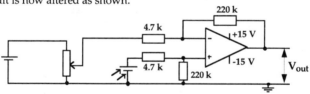

i) What mode is the op-amp operating in now?
ii) With the lamp still unlit the potentiometer is adjusted.
Explain how this circuit enables the output voltage to be set to zero.
iii) The lamp is switched on and the output voltage is now 1.50 V.
Calculate the voltage which the solar cell produces.

7. The circuit is designed to give a voltmeter reading when a load is applied to the strain gauge.

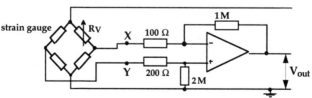

a) Explain the purpose of the variable resistor, R_V.
b) Sketch a graph showing how the p.d. between X and Y is related to small changes in the resistance of the strain gauge.
c) If the p.d. between X and Y is 0.3 mV, calculate the output voltage.

Alternating Current and Voltage

Exercise 6.1 Peak and r.m.s.

1. The r.m.s. current from a mains supply is I.
   What is the peak current?

2. Mains electricity is supplied to our homes at 230 V r.m.s.
   What is the peak value of this voltage?

3. An oscilloscope connected across a 2 Ω resistor records a peak voltage of 5 V.
   What is the value of the r.m.s. current through the resistor?

4. An alternating current of r.m.s. 2 A flows through a resistor. A steady direct current I in an identical resistor generates heat at the same rate as the first resistor.
   State the value of I?

5. An immersion heater is used to heat water in an insulated container. An a.c. supply and a d.c. supply both produce the same rate of heating from the heater. The a.c. supply has a peak voltage of 10 V.
   Calculate the p.d. of the d.c. supply.

6. The output voltage from a step-down mains transformer is to be monitored.
   a) What instrument would you use to measure the r.m.s. voltage of the supply?
   b) What instrument would you use to measure the peak voltage of the supply?
   c) If the r.m.s. voltage is 12 V, what is the peak voltage?

7. The graph represents a sinusoidal alternating voltage.
   a) Calculate the r.m.s. voltage.
   b) If the voltage is applied to a 3.3 kΩ resistor, find the peak current through the resistor.

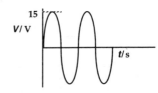

8. An immersion heater can be operated either from an a.c. supply or a d.c. supply. The graph represents the a.c. supply voltage.
   What d.c. supply would produce the same rate of heating from this heater?

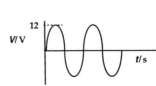

9. In the specification of a certain non-electrolytic capacitor the maximum operating voltage is given as 63 V d.c.
   What therefore is the greatest r.m.s. voltage allowed when this capacitor is used in an a.c. circuit?

10. An a.c. voltage has a d.c. equivalent voltage of 15 V.
    Calculate the peak voltage.

Exercise 6.2   Frequency

Questions 1 to 3 refer to the following diagrams which represent oscilloscope screens, with the grid lines all 1 cm apart.

Diagram A

Diagram B

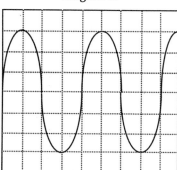 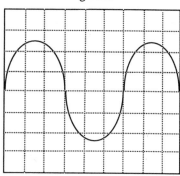

1. Diagram **A** represents an a.c. supply.
    The voltage gain is set at 5 V cm^{-1} and the time base at 5 ms cm^{-1}.
    a) What is the peak voltage of the supply?
    b) What is the r.m.s. voltage of the supply?
    c) What is the frequency of the supply?

2. Diagram **B** represents an a.c. supply.
    The voltage gain is set at 20 V cm^{-1} and the time base at 2.5 ms cm^{-1}.
    a) What is the peak voltage of the supply?
    b) What is the r.m.s. voltage of the supply?
    c) What is the frequency of the supply?

3. If diagram **A** represents the mains voltage, calculate
    a) the setting of the voltage gain of the oscilloscopes, in V cm^{-1},
    b) the time base setting of the oscilloscope, in ms cm^{-1}.

4. An alternating signal is applied to an oscilloscope which has its time-base set at 10 ms cm^{-1}. Two complete waves appear on the screen, which is 4 cm wide, as shown. The time base setting is changed with all other controls kept the same as before.

    State how many waves will appear on the screen when
    a) the time-base is set at 1 ms cm^{-1},
    b) the time-base is set at 5 ms cm^{-1},
    c) the time-base is set at 20 ms cm^{-1},
    d) the time-base is set at 50 ms cm^{-1}.

Exercise 6.3 Mixed Problems

1. A resistor **R** is connected in a circuit as shown. The frequency of the alternating supply can be varied but the peak voltage is kept constant.

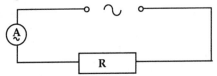

Sketch a graph which shows the relationship between the r.m.s. current *I* in the resistor and the frequency *f* of the supply.

2. An oscilloscope is connected in a circuit as shown.

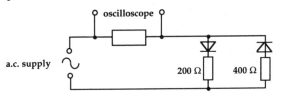

Sketch the trace obtained on the oscilloscope.

3. An oscilloscope being used as a voltmeter has its time base switched **off** and its Y-gain set at 2 V cm^{-1}. The trace obtained is shown.

What is the value of the peak voltage being measured?

4. An a.c. supply of 1 V peak value and a d.c. supply of 7 V are connected in series as shown.

Sketch the trace which could be seen on the oscilloscope with the time base suitably adjusted to show two complete waves of the a.c. supply. (Numerical values should be shown on the voltage axis.)

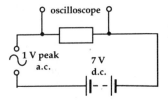

5. The trace shown is produced by a signal generator on an oscilloscope screen, with 1 cm squares.

a) The Y-gain is set at 20 V cm^{-1}.
    Calculate the peak voltage of the signal generator.

b) The time-base is set at 10^{-3} s cm^{-1}.
    Calculate the frequency of the signal generator.

c) How many squares in **each** direction would be required to display one complete wave of mains voltage if the controls remain on the same settings?

6. The diagram illustrates an experiment to compare the a.c. and d.c. voltages which will produce the same brightness in the lamp.

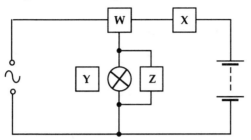

a) Name the pieces of apparatus marked **W, X, Y,** and **Z**.
b) Explain how the bulb is connected to the a.c. supply and then to the d.c. supply.
c) Explain how the brightness of the bulb when connected to the a.c. supply can be measured.
d) How can the brightness of the bulb be changed when connected to the d.c. supply?
e) When the a.c. and d.c. brightnesses are the same, what would you expect to see on the screen of component **Z**?

Capacitors

Exercise 7.1   Capacitance

1. The graph shows how the charge **Q** on a capacitor is related to the p.d. **V** applied across its plates.

   a) What does the shaded area under the graph represent?
   b) What does the gradient of the graph represent?

2. A capacitor takes 320 µC to fully charge when connected to an 8 V supply.

   Calculate the capacitance of the capacitor.

3. "A capacitor has a capacitance of 4 microfarads."

   Explain what is meant by this statement.

4. Which of the following units is equivalent to a farad?

   A. V   **B.** C   **C.** CV   **D.** CV^{-1} **E.** VC^{-1}

5. In the circuit shown the capacitor **C** is charged with a steady current of 1 mA by carefully adjusting the variable resistor **R**.

   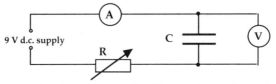

   The voltmeter reading is taken every 10 s. The results are shown in the table.

Time/s	0	10	20	30	40
Voltage/V	0	1.9	4.0	6.2	8.1

   Plot a graph of charge against voltage for the capacitor and hence find its capacitance.

6. In the circuit shown **C** is a 1.0 µF capacitor holding a charge of 10^{-5} C and **R** is a 10 Ω resistor.

   a) Calculate the voltage across the capacitor.
   b) Calculate the initial current flowing in the circuit when the switch is closed.

   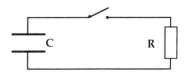

7. After the switch is closed in the circuit shown, the variable resistor **R** is adjusted to give a constant charging current of 2.0 x 10⁻⁵ A for a time of 30 s.
During this time the p.d. across the capacitor rises from 0 V to 9 V.

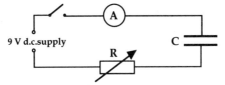

9 V d.c.supply

a) What change must be made to the variable resistor **R**?
b) Calculate the capacitance of the capacitor.

8. The circuit shown is set up to investigate the charging of a capacitor.

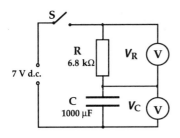

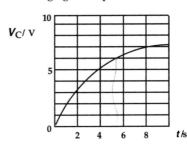

At the start of the experiment the capacitor is uncharged. The graph shows how the p.d. V_C across the capacitor varies with time from the instant the switch **S** is closed.

a) Draw a graph showing how the p.d. V_R across the resistor varies with time during the first 10 s of charging.
   (Numerical values are required on both axes.)
b) Calculate the current in the circuit at the instant the p.d. across the capacitor is 6.0 V.

9. The switch **K** is made to vibrate between contacts **X** and **Y** at a rate of 50 complete vibrations (to and fro) per second. The voltmeter reads 10.0 V and the milliammeter **A** reads 8.00 mA.

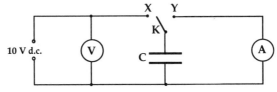

a) How much charge passes through the milliammeter in 1 s?
b) How much charge passes through the milliammeter each time the switch makes contact with **Y**?
c) Calculate the capacitance of the capacitor **C**?

10. The circuit shown is used to find the capacitance of a capacitor.

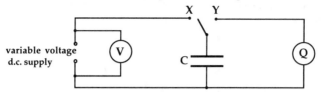

With the switch in position **X**, the capacitor charges up to the supply voltage. The reading on the voltmeter is noted and the switch is moved to position **Y**. The coulombmeter **Q** then indicates the charge stored by the capacitor.

a) One set of results is:

Voltmeter reading   =   1.5 V

Coulombmeter reading   =   24 μC

Use these results to calculate a value for the capacitance of the capacitor.

b) The experiment is repeated with the **same** capacitor for five different values of the supply voltage, giving the following values for the capacitance:

16 μF, 18 μF, 20 μF, 16 μF, 15 μF

Using these five results, calculate the mean value for the capacitance **and** the approximate random uncertainty in this value.

c) How could the approximate random uncertainty in the mean value of the capacitance be reduced?

11. An uncharged capacitor is connected in the circuit shown.

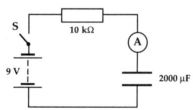

a) Describe the response of the ammeter after the switch **S** is closed.

b) How would you know when the potential difference across the capacitor is at its maximum?

c) Suggest a suitable range for the ammeter.

(Hint: Calculate the maximum current.)

d) If the 10 kΩ resistor is replaced by one of a larger resistance, what will be the effect on the maximum potential difference across the capacitor?

e) If the 2000 μF capacitor is replaced by one of a larger capacitance, what will be the effect on the maximum potential difference across the capacitor?

Exercise 7.2   Energy in Capacitors

1. When a capacitor **C** is connected to a supply of potential difference **V**, it stores a charge **Q**.
    Give **three** possible formulae for the energy stored in the capacitor.

2. A capacitor has a rating of 220 pF, 10 V. It is used at its rated voltage.
    a) Calculate the charge stored on the capacitor.
    b) Calculate the energy stored by the capacitor.

3. A capacitor is marked "Electrolytic 2000 μF, 16 V".

    a) How much charge does it store when fully charged?
    b) How much energy does it store when fully charged?
    c) What does the word "Electrolytic" tells you about this capacitor.
    d) What might happen if a potential difference much greater than 16 V were applied across its terminals?

4. An initially uncharged capacitor is charged using a constant current of 90 μA.
    After 100 s the voltage across the capacitor is 12 V.
    a) How much charge is stored on the capacitor after 100 s?
    b) How much energy is stored on the capacitor after 100 s?
    c) A second capacitor with a larger capacitance is charged for the same time using the same current.
    i)   How does the voltage across the second capacitor compare with the first?
    ii) How does the energy stored in the second capacitor compare with the first?

5. A capacitor is connected to a circuit and the graph shown is obtained.

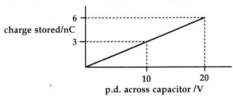

    a) Draw the circuit which could have been used.
    b) Calculate the capacitance of the capacitor.
    c) Calculate the energy stored by the capacitor when charged to a p.d. of 10 V.
    d) Calculate the energy stored by the capacitor when charged to a p.d. of 20 V.

6. An 800 μF capacitor is fully charged at a p.d. of 12 V.

    a) The capacitor is removed from the circuit and connected across a 10 Ω resistor.
    What is the total energy dissipated in the resistor?
    b) In another experiment, the fully charged capacitor is connected across a 20 Ω resistor instead of the 10 Ω resistor.
    How does the energy dissipated in this resistor compare with that calculated in part **a)**?
    You must justify your answer.

7. The diagram shows the flash-lamp circuit for a camera.

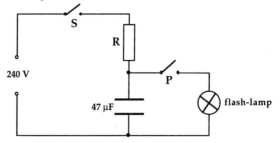

a) Initially the capacitor is uncharged and switches **S** and **P** are open.
   Switch **S** is now closed.
   i) Calculate the energy stored in the capacitor when it is fully charged.
   ii) When the camera shutter is operated, switch **S** is opened and switch **P** is
       closed. The capacitor now fully discharges through the flash-lamp in a
       time of 1.6 ms.
       What is the average power developed in the flash-lamp?
b) The following information is marked on the capacitor: 47 µF; 300 V.
   This means that the maximum voltage that should be applied across the capacitor
   is 300 V.
   i) Why does the capacitor have a maximum voltage?
   ii) Could this capacitor be safely connected to a 230 V a.c. supply?
       Justify your answer.

8. A neon lamp lights when the voltage across it rises to 80 V and goes out when the
voltage falls to 60 V. In the circuit shown , the 0.4 µF capacitor is connected in series
with a 500 KΩ resistor to a 100 V d.c. supply. When the switch **S** is closed
the neon lamp flashes at a frequency of 8 Hz.

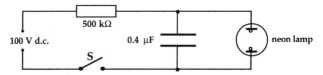

a) Calculate the charge stored in the capacitor when the voltage across it is
   i) 80 V,
   ii) 60 V.
b) Determine the energy dissipated in each flash of the neon lamp.
c) Sketch the waveform which would be seen on a suitably adjusted oscilloscope
   connected across the neon lamp.
d) If the value of the resistor is increased, the frequency of the flashing neon lamp
   changes.
   How would the value of the capacitor require to be changed to restore the
   frequency to its original value?
e) The flash frequency could also have been restored to its original value by increasing
   the supply voltage. Explain this.
f) If the supply voltage is in increased further, the neon lamp stays on all the time.
   Explain why this happens.

Exercise 7.3   Charge, Discharge Characteristics

1. The circuit shows an uncharged 470 μF capacitor in series with a 1.2 kΩ resistor.
    An oscilloscope is connected across the resistor.

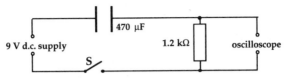

    a) Calculate the initial current in the resistor after the switch **S** is closed.
    b) Calculate the final charge on the capacitor.
    c) Calculate the energy stored on the capacitor.
    d) Draw the graph of the voltage across the capacitor against time for the charging
        period. (Numerical values are only required on the voltage axis.)
    e) Draw the graph of the current against time for the charging period.
        (Numerical values are only required on the current axis.)

2. You are given a capacitor, a battery, two resistors, a two way switch, an ammeter, an
    oscilloscope and connecting wires. You are asked to set up a circuit which would allow
    you to look at the variation of current and voltage across the capacitor on charging
    and discharging the capacitor.

    a) Draw a diagram of the circuit you would use.
    b) Explain how the circuit operates to show both charge and discharge characteristics.
    c) Draw the graphs that would be obtained, explaining carefully which graphs show
        charging and which show discharging.

3. Each of the following graphs shows either voltage across a capacitor against time or
    current against time when a capacitor is either charged or discharged.

    For each graph state whether the current or voltage is plotted on the y-axis and
    whether the capacitor is charging or discharging.

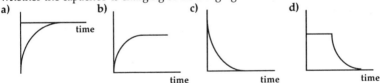

4. By moving the switch **K** in the circuit shown
    from **X** to **Y** the capacitor **C** may be
    discharged through a variable resistor **R**
    and a sensitive meter **G**.
    In one such discharge the meter shows a
    maximum deflection of 5 units and it took
    8 s for the reading to become 1 unit.

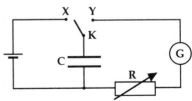

    a) If **R** is set at a decreased value, suggest
        values for the maximum deflection and the
        time to reduce to 1 unit.
    b) If **R** is set at an increased value, suggest
        values for the maximum deflection and the
        time to reduce to 1 unit.

5. The circuit shown is used to charge a capacitor and the graphs show the variation of current *I* with time *t*, and voltage *V* with time *t*.

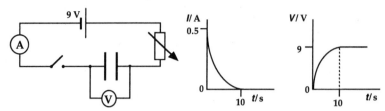

a) The capacitor is discharged and the value of the variable resistor is **increased**. The experiment is then repeated.
Copy the two graphs shown and sketch the **new** current-time graph and voltage-time graph on the same axes.
b) The capacitor is discharged and the value of the variable resistor is **decreased below the original value**. The experiment is then repeated.
Copy the two graphs shown and sketch the **new** current-time graph and voltage-time graph on the same axes.

6. The circuit shown was set up to investigate the charge-discharge characteristics of the capacitor. The 6 V supply has negligible internal resistance.
Initially the capacitor is uncharged and the switch is in position **Y**. The switch is moved to position **X** until the capacitor is fully charged and then finally back to **Y**.

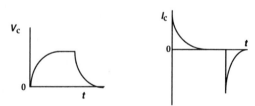

The graphs show the p.d. V_c across the capacitor and the current I_c in the ammeter during this process.

a) State the value of the p.d. across the capacitor when fully charged.
b) Calculate the maximum current during the charging process.
c) Sketch a graph showing how the p.d. across resistor **R** varies with time during the charging process.
(Numerical values are not required.)
d) Is the resistance of the lamp bigger or smaller than 800 Ω?
Justify your answer.
e) Calculate the energy stored in the capacitor when it is fully charged.

7. The capacitor in the circuit shown is fully charged at a certain voltage, **V**.

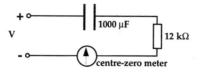

Describe how the current to the centre-zero meter changes when the power supply voltage **V** is

a) increased slightly to a new steady value,
b) decreased slightly to a new steady value.

8. A pupil sets up the apparatus shown to measure how long it takes a ball to travel between two thin strips of metal foil on a track. The ball breaks each foil in turn as it rolls past.

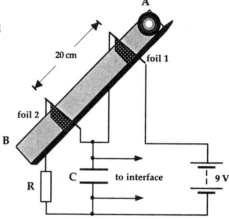

A computer with an appropriate interface is used to monitor and display the voltage across the capacitor **C**.

a) What will be the voltage across the capacitor before foil **1** is broken?
b) What happens in the circuit after foil **1** is broken?
c) When foil **2** is broken, the voltage across the capacitor is 2 V.
  i) Draw a graph of voltage against time to show the computer display as the ball rolls from **A** to **B**.
  (Numerical values are required on the voltage axis.)
  ii) Indicate on the time axis of your graph, the region which corresponds to the ball travelling between the foils.

9. A roads engineer uses the circuit
    shown to produce a flashing light
    which acts as a hazard warning
    indicator during work operations.

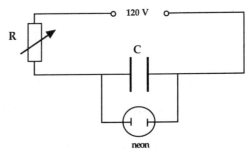

When the p.d. across the neon bulb increases to 90 V it lights up and stays lit until the
p.d. decreases to 70 V. She connects an oscilloscope across the neon bulb and obtains
the following trace.

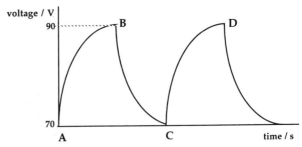

a) Explain what is happening at each of the following sections of the trace.
   i)   AB
   ii) BC
   iii) CD
b) State **one** method of **decreasing** the frequency of flashes of the neon bulb.

Exercise 7.4   Capacitors in a.c.

1. The circuits below contain identical signal generators.

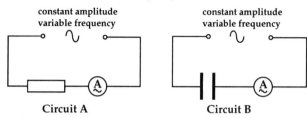

constant amplitude
variable frequency

constant amplitude
variable frequency

Circuit A   Circuit B

   a) Sketch the graph of current against frequency for circuit **A**.
   b) Sketch the graph of current against frequency for circuit **B**.
   c) In circuit **B**, explain how an alternating current can flow in the circuit when the space
      between the plates of the capacitor is an insulator.

2. The circuit shows a capacitor connected to a
    lamp and a signal generator kept at constant
    amplitude.

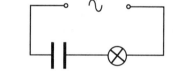

   a) State what happens to the brightness
      of the lamp when the frequency of the
      supply is increased.
      Explain this observation.
   b) What happens to the brightness of the lamp if the a.c. supply is replaced by an
      equivalent d.c. supply?

3. When the circuit below is set up, the frequency of the constant amplitude supply
    is 1 kHz. The trace on the oscilloscope is also shown.

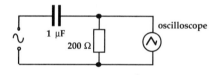

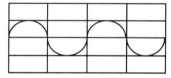

    The frequency is now increased to 2 kHz while the oscilloscope controls are left
    untouched.

    Make a sketch, with grid lines as shown, of the trace you would now expect to see on
    the oscilloscope.

4. A pupil notices the following filter network in the circuit diagram for her new stereo
    amplifier.

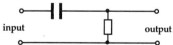

    input   output

    Explain whether this filter is intended to remove low frequency "rumble" or high
    frequency "hiss."

Revision Questions for Higher Physics   **Page 79**

Optics

Exercise 8.1   Waves

1. State a test for wave motion.

2. When a light wave travels from the air into water, state what happens to
    a) the wavelength,
    b) the frequency,
    c) the velocity.

3. A microwave oven, used to cook a steak, produces microwaves of frequency 2450 MHz.
    a) Calculate the wavelength of these microwaves in a vacuum.
    b) State how the wavelength will be affected when the microwaves enter the steak.

4. a) What are the **four** main properties of wave motion?
    b) Which of these proves wave motion is taking place?
    c) Describe how you would show experimentally that light has wave properties.

5. The audible frequency range of a boy's hearing is 30 Hz to 16 500 Hz.

    If the speed of sound in air is 340 m s^{-1}, what is the shortest wavelength of sound in air which the boy can hear?

6. Sketch a graph which shows how the frequency of sound varies with the wavelength of sound.
    Assume the speed of sound is constant for all frequencies.

7. a) Give the electromagnetic spectrum in order of increasing frequency.
    b) State the colours of the visible spectrum in order of increasing wavelength.

8. The velocity of sound in a metal is 11 times the velocity of sound in air.
    The wavelength of a certain note in air is 2 m.

    What is the wavelength of the same note in the metal?

9. The diagram represents a wave of frequency f and wavelength λ moving with speed c.

    What is the time taken for the crest of the wave shown at position **P** to reach position **Q**? Give your answer in terms of λ and c.

    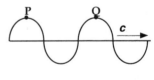

10. A generator of frequency 25 Hz produces waves as shown.

    a) What is the wavelength of the waves?
    b) Calculate the speed of the waves.
    c) If the frequency is doubled to 50 Hz, what will happen to the wavelength? State the assumption which you make.

    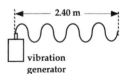

Exercise 8.2   Path Difference

1. An interference pattern is produced when two coherent waves overlap.
    a) If a minimum is produced, what are the possible values for the path difference?
    b) If a maximum is produced, what are the possible values for the path difference?

2. S_1 and S_2 are coherent sources of microwaves of wavelength λ.

    If a maximum signal is detected at **X**, suggest **two** different possibilities for the path difference.

3. The figure shows the paths of light in a double slit interference experiment. Waves from two slits S_1 and S_2 produce a bright fringe at **P**.
    The figure also indicates a series of bright and dark fringes.
    The light has a wavelength of 400 nm.

    Calculate the path difference $S_1 P - S_2 P$.

    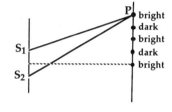

4. A microwave transmitter is directed at a metal plate which has two slits **P** and **Q** as shown. The microwave radiation had a wavelength of 3 cm. A microwave receiver is moved from **R** to **S** and in doing so detects maxima and minima of intensity at the positions shown.

    What is the path difference between **PR** and **QR**?

    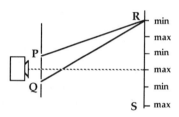

5. Two loudspeakers are connected to the same signal generator as shown.
    A microphone at **X** detects maximum intensity. When the microphone is moved slowly upwards, it detects the first minimum at **Y**.

    Calculate the wavelength of the sound emitted from the loudspeakers.

    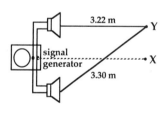

6. S_1 and S_2 are two coherent wave sources giving an interference pattern along the line **XY**. **O** is the central (zero) maximum, **P** the first maximum, **Q** the second maximum and **R** the third maximum. The first maximum **P** occurs where $S_1 P = 20$ cm and $S_2 P = 18$ cm.

    What is the path difference for the third maximum ($S_1 R - S_2 R$)?

    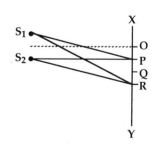

7. Microwaves of wavelength 2.8 cm pass through two narrow gaps G_1 and G_2 in an aluminium barrier. Point **P** on the far side of the barrier is 11.2 cm further from one gap than the other.

   Explain whether point **P** is a maximum or a minimum.

   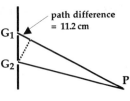

8. Two water-wave generators, S_1 and S_2, produce water waves of wavelength 2 m. S_1 and S_2 are placed 4 m apart in a water tank as shown. There is a detector on the water surface at **P**, 3 m from S_1. Each generator on its own produces waves of amplitude **y** at position **P**.

   When both are operating together and in phase, what is the amplitude of the wave at **P**?

   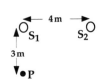

9. A microwave source produces 2.8 cm waves. When a metal reflector is placed as shown, an interference pattern is observed with **X** being on a line of **constructive interference**.

   If **OX** = 40 cm, suggest **two** possible values for the total path length **OYX**.

   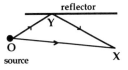

10. Two loudspeakers are arranged as shown and both emit a note of frequency 1000 Hz. When a pupil moves from **X** to **Y**, the note he hears alternates between loud and quiet.

    Give **two** ways in which successive loud regions can be made closer together.

    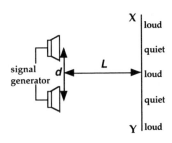

11. In a water tank, circular water waves are produced by two dippers **A** and **B**, which move up and down in phase. An interference pattern is observed with a minimum at **P**.

    If the distances are as shown, explain which of the following values could be the wavelength of the waves: **2, 3, 4, 6 cm**

    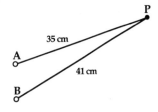

12. Consider the following passage in which **three** words are missing and have been replaced by the letters **X, Y** and **Z**.
    "When waves from two coherent sources of **X** light (i.e. light of one frequency) combine, it is observed that **Y** occurs. The resulting pattern varies in brightness. The brightness depends on the combined **Z**"

    State which words are represented by the letters **X, Y** and **Z**.

13. Loudspeakers **1** and **2** are both connected to the same signal generator which is set to produce a 1 kHz signal. Loudspeaker **1** is switched on but loudspeaker **2** is switched off.

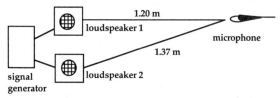

State **and** explain what happens to the amplitude of the signal picked up by the microphone when loudspeaker **2** is switched on.
Your explanation should include a calculation, taking the value of the speed of sound in air to be 340 m s^{-1}.

14. In an experiment, microwaves from a transmitter are reflected by a metal plate. Between the transmitter and the reflector is a diode probe connected to a microammeter. The diode probe picks up microwaves and the microammeter reading is a measure of the intensity of the microwaves.

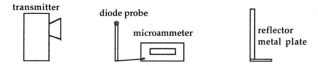

The graph shows how the microammeter reading varies as the **reflector** is moved to the right.

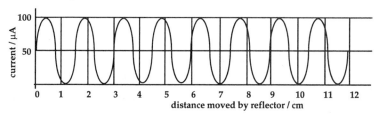

a) Explain why movement of the reflector causes the maxima and minima shown on the graph.
b) What is the wavelength of the microwaves?
c) In another experiment with a different source of microwaves, a maximum reading was found with the reflector at 22.5 cm from the detector and a further ten maxima were found as the reflector was moved to a maximum reading at 36.5 cm from the detector.
 i) Calculate the wavelength of these microwaves.
 ii) What was the frequency of these microwave?

Exercise 8.3   Prisms and Diffraction Gratings

1. A narrow beam of white light is passed through a triangular glass prism as shown in diagram **1**. The prism is then replaced by a diffraction grating as shown in diagram **2**.

narrow beam of white light

glass prism

screen

Diagram 1

narrow beam of white light

diffraction grating

screen

Diagram 2

   a) Describe in detail what would be seen on the screen in diagram **1**.
   b) Describe in detail what would be seen on the screen in diagram **2**.

2. State a possible wavelength for
   a) red light,
   b) green light,
   c) blue light.

3. Part of the visible spectrum in air is shown.

| red | yellow | blue |

   How do the following wave characteristics vary as the light changes from red to blue (in the direction of the arrow)?
   a) wavelength
   b) frequency
   c) speed

4. Light of wavelength 600 nm is passed through a grating.
   The grating has 2.5×10^5 lines per metre.

   Calculate the angle at which the first maximum appears.

5. A green filter is placed in front of a source of white light. The filtered light is viewed through a diffraction grating with 100 lines per millimetre. A pattern of bright and dark fringes is observed but they are too close together for accurate measurement.

   For each of the following changes, explain whether the fringe separation would increase or decrease.
   a) increasing the distance between the grating and the screen
   b) using a blue filter instead of a green one
   c) using a more intense light source
   d) using a grating with 300 lines per millimetre

6. During an experiment, white light is dispersed into its constituent colours and the red light is deviated the most.

   a) What has been used to cause the dispersion?
   b) How many spectra will be produced, only one or several pairs?

7. Red light from a laser is passed through double slits. The diagram shows the pattern of dots produced on a screen. Each pair of dots are *x* apart.

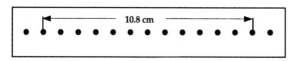

Other measurements are:
Distance from slits to screen, **D** = 3.02 m
Wavelength of laser light λ = 633 nm

a) Using the expression $\lambda = \dfrac{x\,d}{D}$ calculate the separation of the slits **d**.

b) What change in the spacing of the dots will take place if a laser emitting green light is used instead?

8. a) Using monochromatic light, interference fringes are produced on a screen which is 2 m from a pair of narrow slits. The slits are 0.5 mm apart and the fringe separation is 1.6 mm.

Given the formula

$$\lambda = \frac{x\,d}{D}$$ where **x** = separation between two fringes (m)
d = slit separation (m)
D = distance between slit and screen (m)
calculate the wavelength of light used.

b) The screen is now placed 4 m from the slits and the slit separation is reduced to 0.1 mm. Calculate the new fringe separation.

9. A biologist is studying the effect of different colours of light on a sample of chlorophyll. He used a diffraction grating with 6.0×10^5 lines per metre to produce a first order spectrum of sunlight as shown.

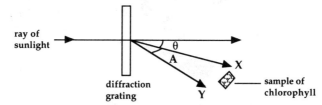

a) i) Explain briefly how a diffraction grating produces a continuous spectrum from a ray of sunlight.

ii) The wavelength of the light at the end X of the spectrum is 410 nm. Calculate the value of the angle θ.

iii) The angle **A** in the diagram above is 9°. Calculate the wavelength at end **Y** of the spectrum.

b) The biologist now uses a triangular glass prism to produce a continuous spectrum from a ray of sunlight.
State **two** differences between this spectrum and the spectrum produced by the grating.

10. The apparatus shown is set up to determine the wavelength of light from a laser.

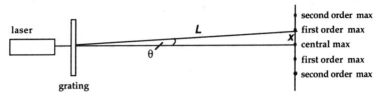

The separation of lines in the grating **d** = 1.693 x 10⁻⁵ m.
The wavelength of light is calculated using the diffraction grating equation
and $\sin \theta = \frac{\lambda}{L}$ where angle θ and distances **x** and **L** are shown above.

Seven students measure the distance **L** with a tape measure.
Their results are as follows:
2.402 m, 2.399 m, 2.412 m, 2.408 m, 2.388 m, 2.383 m, 2.415 m

a) i) Calculate the mean value for **L**.
   ii) Calculate the approximate random uncertainty in the mean of **L**.
b) The best estimate of the distance **x** is 91 ± 1 mm.
   Show by calculation whether **L** or **x** has the larger percentage uncertainty.
c) Calculate the wavelength, in nanometres, of the laser light.
   Give your answer in the form **final value ± absolute uncertainty**.
d) Suggest an improvement which could be made so that a more accurate
   estimate of the wavelength could be made.
   Use only the same equipment and make the same number of measurements.

11. The sketch illustrates one method of producing interference fringes.

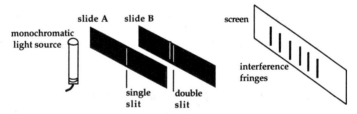

a) For each of the following changes, state the effect on the spacing of the interference
   fringes.
   i) moving the screen further away from slide **B**
   ii) replacing slide **B** by another similar slide with two slits closer together
   iii) replacing the monochromatic light source with one of longer wavelength

b) The monochromatic light source is replaced by a tungsten filament lamp and slide **B**
   is replaced by a diffraction grating.
   i) Explain in terms of waves why the red colour of the observed spectrum is seen
      further away from the central band than the blue colour.
   ii) Explain why the central band, known as the zero order spectrum, is
      white.

Exercise 8.4   Refractive Index

1. The diagram shows a ray of light travelling in a medium of high refractive index and meeting another medium of low refractive index.

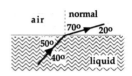

On crossing the boundary between the two media
   a) state whether the ray bends towards or away from the normal,
   b) state whether the wavelength increases, decreases or stays the same,
   c) state whether the frequency increases, decreases or stays the same,
   d) state whether the velocity increases, decreases or stays the same.

2. The diagram shows a ray of light passing from liquid into air.

   Calculate the refractive index of this liquid relative to air.

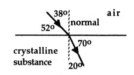

3. The diagram shows a ray of light going from air into a crystalline substance

   Calculate the refractive index of this crystalline substance relative to air.

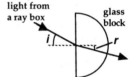

4. A pupil sets up the apparatus shown to investigate the relationship between the angle of incidence i, and the angle of refraction r, for a ray passing from air into glass.

   a) Sketch the graph she would obtain for sin i against sin r.
   b) Explain why a semi-circular glass block was used.

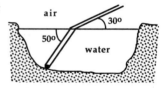

5. The diagram shows a parallel beam of monochromatic light emerging from an underwater spotlight in an ornamental pond.

   What is the absolute refractive index of the water in this pond?

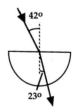

6. The diagram shows the path of a ray of light through a semicircular block of glass. The direction of the ray is shown by the arrows.

   Draw a diagram to show the path of the ray travelling in the reverse direction.

7. Light passes from air into a liquid.

   Give expressions for the refractive index in terms of the angle to the normal, the wavelength and the velocity of the light in the air compared to that in the liquid.

8. Sound waves travel 4.5 times faster in water than they do in air. Sound waves from an undersea earthquake strike the surface of the water at 45° to the normal.

   What angle will the sound waves make to the normal in air?

9. The diagram shows a block of perspex out of which a triangular section has been cut.

   Copy and complete the diagram to show the path of the ray of light.

   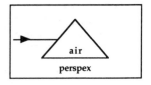

10. A material has a refractive index of 1.5. Light of frequency 6×10^{14} Hz is incident on the material.

    Calculate the speed, wavelength and frequency of the light in the material.

11. Waves travel from medium **A** to medium **B**. In **A** their direction is 45° to the normal and in **B** it is 30° to the normal.

    If the velocity of the waves in medium **A** is 0.283 m s^{-1}, calculate the velocity in medium **B**.

    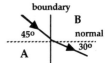

12. A ray of light travels with speed v_1 through medium **1** as shown and then passes into another medium **2**, where it travels at speed v_2. The refractive indices for medium **1** and medium **2** are n_1 and n_2 respectively.

    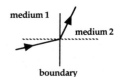

    a) In which medium is the refractive index the greater?
    b) In which medium is the speed of light the greater?

13. A material has a refractive index of 1.4. Light of wavelength 6×10^{-7} m is incident on the material at an angle of 60° to the normal.

    Calculate the speed, wavelength and frequency of the light in the material and the angle the ray makes with the normal in the material.

14. Solid **A** and liquid **B** have the same refractive index.

    What would happen to the speed and wavelength of a light wave passing from the liquid to the solid?

15. The diagram shows a ray of light travelling through air, glass and water, **not** necessarily in that order.

    If light travels faster in water than in glass, then identify medium **1**, medium **2** and medium **3**.

    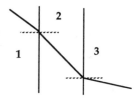

16. The table gives the results of an experiment on the refraction of light travelling through a semi-circular plastic block into air.

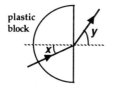

angle x / °	angle y / °
15	23
20	31
31	50
35	61
40	76

   a) State the mathematical relationship between the two angles x and y and show that the results are in agreement with this relationship.
   b) Calculate the refractive index of the plastic.

17. A ray of white light is incident on a glass prism as shown.

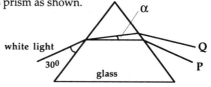

The refractive index of the glass is 1.53 for blue light and 1.51 for red light.

   a) If **P** and **Q** represent the ends of the visible spectrum, which is the blue end?
   b) Calculate angle α.
   c) From the refractive indices, deduce whether red or blue light travels faster through the glass. Give your reasoning.

18. The diagram (**not** to scale) shows the ray **AOB** traced by a pupil investigating the refraction of red light using a semi-circular glass block.

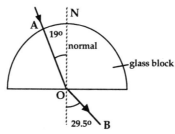

   a) Use the information given in the diagram to calculate the refractive index of glass for red light.
   b) Draw an accurate diagram to show the path of the ray if angle **AON** is increased to 30°.
   c) Calculate the speed of red light in glass.

Exercise 8.5   Critical Angle

1. The refractive index of certain substance is 1.7, relative to air.
    Calculate the critical angle.

2. The refractive index of diamond is 2.42, relative to air.
    Calculate the critical angle.

3. Monochromatic light has a wavelength of 600 nm in air and enters a liquid where its
    wavelength is 400 nm.
    a) Calculate the refractive index of the liquid.
    b) Calculate the critical angle for the light in this liquid.

4   a) What is meant by total internal reflection and under what conditions does it occur?
    b) Draw a diagram showing the path of a ray of light through a short curved section
       of optical fibre.

5. A ray of monochromatic light passes from
    one medium into another as shown.

    a) State the relationship which expresses the
       refractive index in terms of the velocity of
       light in the two media.
    b) If the refractive index of the two materials are
       1.33 and 1.5, respectively, calculate the refractive
       index for light going from medium 1 to medium 2.
    c) Determine the critical angle between the two media.
    d) In which substance does total internal reflection occur?

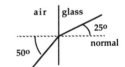

6. A ray of red light travels from air into glass as shown.
    Calculate the critical angle for the glass.

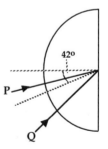

7. A pupil allows two narrow beams of red light, P and Q,
    to enter a semi-circular glass block as shown. Three
    beams are observed by the pupil after the light strikes
    the glass-air boundary.

    Sketch and complete the diagram to show the path
    of the beams after striking the glass-air boundary.
    (Assume the critical angle for the glass is 42º.)

8. Copy each of the following diagrams accurately and complete the path of the ray of light through the block (diagrams are **not** to scale).
The refractive index is stated in each case.

a) n = 1.59

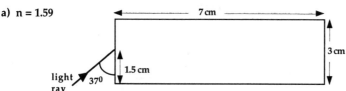

b) n = 1.4

c) n = 1.8

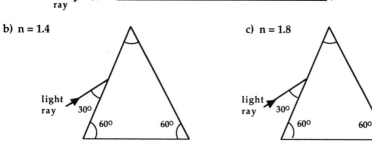

d) n = 1.5

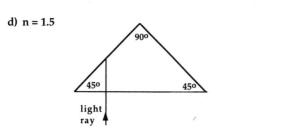

9. Monochromatic light from a ray box is incident on a semi-circular transparent glass block. A diagram of the arrangement is shown.

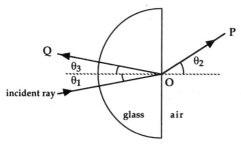

Describe in detail what happens to rays **OP** and **OQ** as the angle θ_1 is slowly increased from the angle shown up to 90°.

Exercise 8.6   Mixed Problems

1. A hollow prism made of thin glass has air inside it. The prism is immersed in a tank of water as shown. All the angles of the prism are 60°. A ray of light is incident on the prism at an angle of 22.1° to the normal.

n water = 1.33

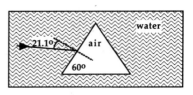

a) Draw a diagram to show the path of the ray through the prism until it emerges into the water again.
b) Calculate the angle at which the ray emerges into the water.

2. Light of wavelength 600 nm in a vacuum enters glass of refractive index 2.0.
    Copy and complete the table below.

Medium	Speed/m s^{-1}	Wavelength/nm	Frequency/Hz
Vacuum			
Glass			

3. A pupil finds a glass prism of the shape shown when she dismantles an old optical instrument. To investigate the optical properties of the prism, she directs a narrow beam of red light towards the prism.

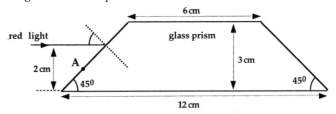

    The glass prism has a refractive index of 1.52 for this red light.

    a) Calculate the value for the critical angle for this light in the glass prism.
    b) Draw a scale diagram of the prism with the dimensions stated.
       Draw the path taken by the light beam through the prism until after it emerges from other side.
       Mark on your diagram the values of all relevant angles.
    c) A second beam of light, parallel to the first and of the same wavelength, is now directed towards the prism at **A**.
       Add to your diagram the complete path taken by this beam through the prism.
    d) How would this prism have affected the view seen by looking through the optical instrument?

4. A student, investigating the concentration of the contents of biological cells, trapped a sample of liquid from the cells under a glass cube as shown.

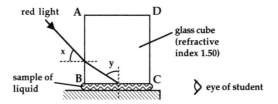

A ray of light from outside and in a vertical plane parallel to one face of the cube was allowed to strike the vertical face **AB** of the cube at varying angles of incidence. The incident light was initially examined with a spectrometer, using a diffraction grating with 600 lines per millimetre. There were two colours of light used.
Colour **1** was detected at an angle of 24.5° and colour **2** at 17.0°.

a) Calculate the wavelength of colour **1** and state the colour.
b) Calculate the wavelength of colour **2** and state the colour.
c) Then the student examined the light passing through the sample of liquid. She found that using colour **1** the liquid appeared bright only when the angle of incidence x was greater than 48.6°.
With the aid of diagrams explain why the liquid appears
   i)   bright when x is greater than 48.6°,
   ii) dark when x is less than 48.6°.
d) Calculate the angle **y** when x is 48.6°.
e) If the student repeated the experiment using colour **2** instead of colour **1**, how would this affect the angle **x** at which the liquid goes bright?
Explain your answer.

5. Monochromatic light of wavelength 600 nm enters a liquid where the wavelength is found to be 400 nm.

a) Calculate the speed of light in this liquid.
b) Calculate the critical angle in the liquid.
c) Sketch the graph of frequency against wavelength for light.
d) Calculate the frequency of the light in this case.

6. A source of monochromatic light is placed behind a diffraction grating with a slit separation of 0.25 mm. A light detector is moved parallel to the slits on a screen 2.5 m in front of the slits. A series of maxima and minima are produced.

a) Sketch a diagram of the apparatus.
b) Explain how the maximum readings on the detector are produced.
c) If the central maxima is at x = 0 and the 4 th maxima is at 27.9 mm, calculate the wavelength of the light used in the experiment.
d) If the experiment is repeated with a different colour of light, suggest how the wavelength of the light compares with the original if the fourth maxima is now at 24.0 mm from the central position.
e) How could the experimental arrangement be changed to return the fourth maxima to its original position?

Optoelectronics

Exercise 9.1   Intensity

1 a) What is meant by the intensity of light falling on a surface?
   b) State the units of light intensity.
   c) What is meant by the intensity of electromagnetic radiation falling on a surface?

2. Measurement of the intensity of light is taken at a position which is 1 m away from a monochromatic point source of light. The measurement is then repeated at a new position which is 2 m away from the same source.
   a) What difference is observed in the intensity of the light?
   b) What difference is observed in the wavelength of the light?

3. A light meter registers a value of 100 W m^{-2} when placed at a distance of 50 cm from a small bright light source in a dark room.
   a) What value will it register at a distance of 150 cm from the same source?
   b) What value will it register at a distance of 25 cm from the same source?

4. An experiment is set up in a darkened laboratory with a small light bulb B_1 which emits light at power **P**. The light intensity 50 cm from the bulb is 12 W m^{-2}. The experiment is repeated with a different small bulb B_2, which emits light at power 0.5 **P**.

   What is the light intensity 25 cm from this bulb?

5. A solar cell and meter are used to measure the intensity of light from a small lamp. The meter reading is 4 units when the solar cell is 100 cm from the lamp.
   a) Where should the solar cell be placed to increase the reading to 64 units?
   b) What assumption is made about the lamp in the calculation for part **a)**?

6. Which one of the following sets of results could have been obtained from an experiment to investigate the variation of intensity with distance from a point source of light.

	Distance	10 cm	15 cm	20 cm	25 cm	30 cm	35 cm	40 cm
A	Intensity	256	384	512	940	768	896	1024
B	Intensity	256	171	128	102	85	73	64
C	Intensity	256	384	512	640	512	384	256
D	Intensity	256	114	64	41	28	21	16
E	Intensity	256	171	128	102	128	171	256

7. A space probe is positioned 4×10^{11} m from the Sun. It needs solar panels with an area of 4 m^2 to absorb sufficient energy from the Sun to keep it functioning correctly.

   Calculate the area of solar panels which would be needed to keep the probe functioning correctly if it is repositioned
   a) 3×10^{11} m from the Sun,
   b) 6×10^{11} m from the Sun.

8. To investigate how the intensity of light, **I**, varies with the distance, **d**, from the source of light, the apparatus shown is used in a darkened room.

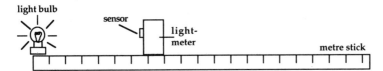

The uncertainty in the light-meter reading is ± 10 units.
The uncertainty in the distance reading is ± 0.5 cm.
The following results are obtained:

Intensity/units	520	300	180	130	80
Distance/m	0.30	0.40	0.50	0.60	0.80

A graph of intensity against distance is plotted and found to be a curve.
However, the results can be used to obtain a straight line graph.

a) On graph paper, plot the straight line graph.
b) State the relationship the graph drawn in part **a)** confirms between **I** and **d**.
c) From your graph deduce where the intensity would have a value of 100 units.
d) Which measurement gives the greatest uncertainty?
e) State the uncertainty in your answer to part **c)**.
f) On the same graph, draw a dotted line to show what would be expected if the experiment were to be repeated with the room lights on.

Exercise 9.2   Photoelectric Effect

Planck's constant, h, = 6.63 x 10^{-34} J s

1. The diagrams show charged gold leaf electroscopes illuminated with electromagnetic radiation.

    In each case, explain whether or not the electroscope will discharge.

    a)   b)   c)   d)

    ultraviolet   ultraviolet   white light   white light

    + + + +   - - - -   + + + +   - - - -

2. Sketch the graph that would be obtained when the photon energy is plotted against photon frequency.

3. A cleaned zinc plate is placed on the cap of a gold leaf electroscope which is then charged negatively.

    a) Explain why the electroscope will discharge when illuminated with dull ultraviolet light.
    b) Explain why the electroscope will **not** discharge when illuminated with intense white light.
    c) What effect will be observed if the ultraviolet light is more intense?

4. A bright red light source and a faint blue light source are shone in turn on a metal surface for the same length of time. Both sources are found to eject electrons from the metal surface.

    a) Explain why electrons ejected by the faint blue light have a greater kinetic energy than those ejected by the bright red light.
    b) Will both light sources eject the same number of electrons?
    Explain your answer.

5. The apparatus shown was set up to demonstrate the photoelectric effect.

    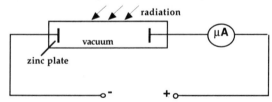

    Sketch the graph showing the relationship between the photoelectric current, I, and the frequency, f, of the radiation.

6. Calculate the energy of a photon of light of wavelength 405 nm.

7. Calculate the wavelength of a photon of energy 4.2 x 10^{-19} J.

8. For each of the following, state whether the statement is true or false.

   a) Photoelectric emission from a metal occurs only if the frequency of the incident radiation is greater than the threshold frequency.

   b) Photoelectric emission takes place when the metal is heated to a very high temperature

   c) The threshold frequency depends on the metal from which photoemission takes place.

   d) If the frequency of the incident radiation is less than the threshold frequency, increasing the intensity will cause photoemission.

   e) If the frequency of the incident radiation is greater than the threshold frequency, increasing the intensity will increase the maximum energy per electron.

   f) If the frequency of the incident radiation is greater than the threshold frequency, increasing the intensity will increase the photoelectron current.

9. Certain metals are observed to emit electrons when irradiated with ultraviolet light.

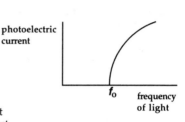

   a) The graph indicates that there is no photoelectric current if the frequency of the light is below a certain value f_0. How can this be explained?

   b) Discuss **briefly** the changes which had to be made to the theory of the nature of light after the discovery of the photoelectric effect.

10. The work function for sodium metal is 2.9×10^{-19} J.
Light of wavelength 5.4×10^{-7} m strikes the surface of this metal.
What is the maximum kinetic energy of the electrons emitted from the surface?

11. The work function of caesium is 2.16×10^{-19} J.
It is illuminated by light of wavelength 589 nm.
What is the maximum velocity with which electrons are emitted from the surface?
(charge on the electron, e, = -1.6×10^{-19} C; mass of the electron, m_e, = 9.11×10^{-31} kg)

12. The minimum energy required by an electron for it to be ejected by the photoelectric effect from the surface of lithium is 3.7×10^{-19} J.

   a) Calculate the minimum frequency which will allow the photoelectric effect to take place.

   b) Is this radiation within the visible spectrum?
Justify your answer.

   c) If light of frequency 6.8×10^{14} Hz is used, determine the maximum kinetic energy of the electrons.

   d) This loss of photoelectrons causes the lithium surface to acquire a positive voltage which, if it becomes large enough, prevents any more electrons being removed from the surface.
Determine the maximum value of this positive voltage.
(charge on the electron, e, = -1.6×10^{-19} C)

Exercise 9.3   Energy Levels

Planck's constant, h, = 6.63×10^{-34} J s

1. A particular atom has energy levels as shown.
    Transitions are possible between all these energy
    levels to produce emission lines in the spectrum.

    a) How many lines are in this spectrum?
    b) i)   Transitions between which two energy levels
            would produce the highest frequency radiation?
       ii) Transitions between which two energy levels
            would produce the longest wavelength radiation?

    ```
    ——————————— E3
    ——————————— E2
    ——————————— E1

    ——————————— ground
                state
    ```

2. The diagram shows the energy levels for
    the hydrogen atom.

    a) Between which two energy levels
       would an electron transition lead to
       emission of radiation of **highest** frequency?
    b) Calculate the frequency of the radiation in
       part (a).

    ```
    ——————————— E4   -0.864 x 10⁻¹⁹ J
    ——————————— E3   -1.360 x 10⁻¹⁹ J
    ——————————— E2   -2.416 x 10⁻¹⁹ J
    ——————————— E1   -5.424 x 10⁻¹⁹ J

    ——————————— E0   -21.76 x 10⁻¹⁹ J
    ```

3. Energy level diagrams for two atoms **A** and **B** are shown to the same scale.

    ```
    ——————————— A2          ——————————— B3
                            ——————————— B2
    ——————————— A1          ——————————— B1

    ——————————— ground      ——————————— ground
                state                   state
    ```

    Electrons are excited to levels A_2 and B_3.

    a) Explain which transition in which atom would give rise to the emission of radiation
       with
       i)   the longest wavelength,
       ii) the highest frequency.
    b) Explain why some lines on the spectrum produced from these transitions are more
       intense than others.

4. The diagram shows the energy levels in an atom.
    Emission lines are produced as excited electrons
    undergo all possible transitions.

    a) What is the maximum number of lines produced
       in this spectrum?
    b) If an electron is excited from energy level E_2 to
       level E_3, what frequency of light is being used
       to excite the electrons?

    ```
    ——————————— E4   -3.8  x 10⁻¹⁹ J
    ——————————— E3   -5.2  x 10⁻¹⁹ J
    ——————————— E2   -9.0  x 10⁻¹⁹ J
    ——————————— E1   -16.4 x 10⁻¹⁹ J

    ——————————— E0   -24.6 x 10⁻¹⁹ J
    ```

5. An electron falls from a high energy level in an atom to another level, E joules below
    it. A photon of light of wavelength λ is emitted.

    If Planck's constant is h and the velocity of light is c, find the wavelength of the
    photon in terms of E, h and c.

6. The table below gives the energy associated with the energy levels available to the orbital electron in a hydrogen atom.

Energy level	Energy / J
1	2.185×10^{-18}
2	3.821×10^{-18}
3	4.124×10^{-18}
4	4.230×10^{-18}
5	4.279×10^{-18}

One series of lines in the hydrogen spectrum involves electrons which have been excited into higher energy levels as shown, falling back to energy level **2**.

a) i) Which transition in **this series** gives rise to the line of longest wavelength?
ii) Calculate the wavelength of this line.
b) In another series of lines, similarly excited electrons return to energy level **1**.
Show that none of the lines in this series is in the visible spectrum.

7. Flood lamps were installed to celebrate the centenary of the Forth Rail bridge. The lamps need 300 kW of electrical power.

a) If 30% of the electrical power is emitted as light of frequency 5.09×10^{14} Hz, calculate the number of photons of this frequency emitted each second.
b) Calculate the wavelength which corresponds to this frequency.
c) If this wavelength is produced by transitions to an energy level of -11.5×10^{-19} J, what is the energy in the higher level?

8. The table lists the energy required to remove an electron from the surface of a number of different metals.

Metal	copper	sodium	potassium	aluminium
Energy/J	7.1×10^{-19}	3.6×10^{-19}	3.5×10^{-19}	6.7×10^{-19}

a) Light is shone on these four metals. The wavelength of the light is gradually increased until only one metal shows the photoelectric effect.
Name this metal.
b) Calculate the minimum frequency of light which will eject an electron from aluminium.
c) The diagram shows three possible energy levels in an atom.
State whether or not transitions between any of these levels produce the photoelectric effect in
i) copper,
ii) potassium.
Justify your answers.

———————— -3.6×10^{-19} J
———————— -5.8×10^{-19} J

———————— -9.5×10^{-19} J

Exercise 9.4   Spectra

Planck's constant, h, = 6.63×10^{-34} J s

1. The emission spectrum of helium contains sharp lines in the violet, blue, yellow orange and red regions of the visible spectrum.

   Explain how these lines are produced.

2. When the spectrum of sunlight is observed, there are two dark lines at wavelengths corresponding to 589.0 nm and 589.6 nm. These are known to be the wavelengths of the two yellow lines seen in the spectrum of hot sodium vapour.

   Explain why the dark lines are present.

3. The diagram shows part of the line spectrum from a hot gas.

red end of spectrum			violet ena of spectrum
X	Y		Z

   Explain why the line **Z** appears much brighter than lines **X** and **Y**.

4. The spectrum of light from a gas discharge tube consists of several distinct coloured lines.

   Explain what this implies about the behaviour of electrons in the atom.

5. Compare the spectrum of white light produced by a household light bulb with the spectrum of light from a mercury vapour lamp.

6. The following statements are about the spectrum of light emitted by the atoms of a gaseous element. State whether each is true or false.

   a) The spectrum emitted by this element is different from the spectrum emitted by another element.
   b) The element emits a continuous spectrum.
   c) The spectrum can be explained if the electrons in the atom are assumed to occupy discrete energy levels.
   d) The electrons in the atom are changing from one energy level to another.
   e) The atom is gradually losing electrons.

7. The following statements are about the spectrum of light obtained by passing white light through a gas. State whether each is true or false.

   a) The dark lines in the spectrum occur at frequencies identical to the frequencies in the line emission spectrum of the gas.
   b) The dark lines are produced by destructive interference.
   c) Photons of light with particular energy values have been absorbed.

8. a) Describe how you would set up apparatus to produce and observe
      i)   a continuous emission spectrum,
      ii) a line emission spectrum,
      iii) an absorption spectrum.
   b) In each of the above cases, explain what would be observed.

9. The diagram shows part of the line emission spectrum of an element.

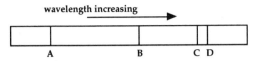

wavelength increasing

A   B   C   D

   a) Light associated with each line is allowed to strike a metal plate in turn and in some cases electrons are ejected from the metal.
      Which of the above spectral lines is most likely to eject electrons from the metal? Justify your answer.
   b) Light of frequency 5.08×10^{14} Hz, corresponding to one of the above lines, can eject electrons with kinetic energy of 0.45×10^{-19} J from the metal plate.
      How much energy is required just to release electrons from the metal?
   c) Show whether or not light of frequency 4.29×10^{14} Hz, corresponding to line **C**, is capable of ejecting electrons from the metal.

10. A sodium vapour lamp emits bright yellow light when electrons make transitions from one energy level to another within the sodium atoms.

   a) State whether the electrons are moving to higher or lower energy levels when the light is emitted.
   b) If the light has a wavelength of 589 nm, calculate the energy difference between these two energy levels in the sodium atom.

11. A Bunsen flame containing vaporised sodium is placed between a sodium vapour lamp and a screen as shown.

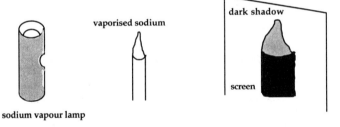

vaporised sodium

dark shadow

screen

sodium vapour lamp

   a) Explain why a dark shadow of the flame is seen on the screen.
   b) The sodium vapour lamp is now replaced with a cadmium vapour lamp.
      Explain why there is now no dark shadow of the flame on the screen.

12. Light from a tungsten vapour lamp is passed through a diffraction grating in a dark-room.

   a) Describe what would be seen on a screen.
   b) The tungsten filament lamp is now replaced by a sodium vapour lamp.
      What will now be seen on the screen?

Exercise 9.5   Lasers

Planck's constant, h, = 6.63 x 10^{-34} J s

1. Laser light is *monochromatic* and *coherent*.

    Briefly explain the meaning of the terms *monochromatic* and *coherent*.

2. The beam of light from a laser is very intense.

    Give **two** reasons for this.

3. The word LASER is an acronym for "light amplification by the stimulated emission of radiation".

    a) Describe what is meant by "stimulated emission".
    b) State **three** ways in which the stimulated photon is identical to the incident photon.
    c) Describe how amplification is produced in a laser.

4. **a)** Draw a labelled diagram of a laser.
    b) Explain the purpose of each mirror in the laser tube.

5. A laser radiates energy when the electrons are stimulated to fall from energy level E_2 to energy level E_1 as shown.

    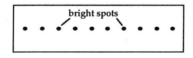

    a) What is the frequency and wavelength of the radiation emitted?
    b) Name the section of the electromagnetic spectrum in which the radiation occurs.

6. A laser is marked with the warning "DANGER: EYE HAZARD".

    a) Why does this laser, which has a power output of only 0.20 mW, present a greater potential eye hazard than a 100 W lamp?
    b) In certain circumstances a laser beam is deliberately directed into the eye. What are these special circumstances?

7. When a laser beam is directed at a diffraction grating a pattern of bright spots is produced on a screen behind the diffraction grating as shown.

    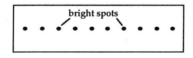

    Explain in terms of the wave nature of light how this pattern is formed.

8. In hospitals, pulsed lasers may be used to repair damage to the retina of the eye. The specification of a typical pulsed laser is:

gas used in laser : argon
duration of pulse : 0.50 ms
energy of one pulse : 0.10 J
wavelength of laser light emitted : 488 nm

The cross-sectional area of the laser beam at the retina is 1.5×10^{-9} m^2.

a) Calculate the light intensity produced at the retina during a pulse of light from this laser.

b) How many photons of light arrive at the retina during one pulse?

9. Infrared radiation from a laser is directed at a small cylinder of copper as shown.

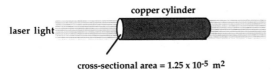

copper cylinder

laser light

cross-sectional area = 1.25×10^{-5} m^2

a) The cylinder has a cross-sectional area of 1.25×10^{-5} m^2. The intensity of the laser beam at the surface of the cylinder is 4.00×10^5 W m^{-2}.
Show that the energy delivered to the cylinder in 100 s is 500 J.

b) The cylinder has a mass of 1.12×10^{-3} kg and the initial temperature of the cylinder is 293 K. Copper melts at 1350 K.
Show by calculation whether or not the 500 J of energy is sufficient to raise the temperature of the copper cylinder to its melting point.
(Energy required to heat copper is given by E = mcΔT, where c = 386 J kg^{-1} °C^{-1}.)

10. The diagram below shows a technique for removing a deposit of fat blocking an artery leading to the heart. Laser light is transmitted along an optical fibre inserted into the artery.

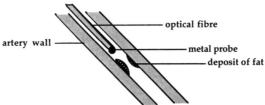

optical fibre

artery wall

metal probe
deposit of fat

The light from the 8 W argon laser used is of 490 nm wavelength.

a) If the metal probe has a mass of 2.5×10^{-4} kg, calculate the time required to supply a pulse of energy necessary to raise its temperature from body temperature to 400 °C.
(Assume that all the light energy is given as heat to the probe.)
(Energy required to heat the metal probe is given by E = mcΔT, where c = 4441 J kg^{-1} °C^{-1}.)

b) Calculate how many photons are required to provide this pulse of energy from the 8 W laser.

Exercise 9.6   Semiconductors

Planck's constant, h, = 6.63 x 10^{-34} J s

1. **a)** Materials may be classified as 'conductors', 'semiconductors' and 'insulators'.
   Give an example of a material from each of these groups.
   b) An electronics textbook states that "... n-type semiconductor material is formed by doping a pure semiconductor with impurity atoms."
   i) What is meant by the term "n-type" semiconductor material?
   ii) What effect does doping always have on the material?

2. An n-type semiconductor is produced by adding arsenic impurity atoms to silicon.
   a) What is the majority charge carrier in the n-type semiconductor?
   b) How many electrons does the arsenic atom have in its outer shell?
   c) What effect does this process have on the resistance of the material?
   d) What effect does this process have on the overall net charge of the material?

3. A sample of p-type semiconductor is compared with a sample of identical size of the pure (undoped) semiconductor material.
   a) What is the majority charge carrier in the p-type semiconductor?
   b) How does the resistance of the p-type compare to the pure semiconductor?
   c) How does the overall net charge of the p-type compare to the pure semiconductor?

4. For each of the following, decide whether the statement is true or false.
   a) In a light emitting diode, positive and negative charge carriers combine to emit light.
   b) In a p-n junction diode, the majority carriers in the p-type material are electrons.
   c) In a photodiode, electron-hole pairs are produced by the action of light.

5. A circuit contains a photodiode and a resistor as shown.·

   For each of the following, decide whether the statement is true or false.
   a) There is a small current in the resistor when light is shone on the photodiode.
   b) There is a small current in the resistor when no light reaches the photodiode.
   c) The photodiode is operating in the photoconductive mode.

6. **a)** Draw the symbol of an n-channel enhancement MOSFET.
   b) Describe the structure of this MOSFET.
   c) How would the device be turned **on**?
   d) What would such a device be used for?

7. State the **two** main uses for a transistor.

8. A student reads the following passage in a physics dictionary.
   "... a solid state device in which positive and negative charge carriers are produced by the action of light on a p-n junction."
   What device is being described?

9. Sketch the graph showing the relationship between current I in a p-n junction diode and the voltage V across the diode.

10. a) Explain how a pure semiconductor is doped to form a p-type semiconductor.
  b) How does this doping affect the electrical properties of the semiconductor material?

11. A potential difference of 0.7 V is maintained across the ends **A** and **B** of the p-n diode as shown.

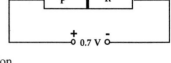

  a) In which direction do the majority of the charge carriers in the p-type material flow?
  b) The recombination of charge carriers in the junction region can be represented by a transition between two energy levels separated by 2.78×10^{-19} J.
  What is the wavelength of the radiation emitted from the junction region?

12. The circuit shows a photodiode connected in series with a resistor and an ammeter. The power supply has an output voltage of 5 V and negligible internal resistance.
In a darkened room, there is no current in the circuit. When light strikes the photodiode, there is a current in the circuit.

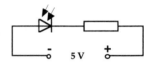

  a) Describe the effect of light on the material of which the photodiode is made.
  b) In which mode is the photodiode operating?
  c) When the photodiode is placed 1.0 m from a small lamp, the current in the circuit is 3.0 μA.
  What is the current in the circuit when the photodiode is placed 75 cm from the same lamp?

13. The power for a space probe is produced by an array of photodiodes. Each photodiode in the array acts as a photovoltaic cell. Under certain conditions the power output of the array is 150 W at 34 V.

  a) Calculate the current produced by the array.
  b) Explain how a photovoltaic cell can produce a small voltage.
  c) What happens to the intensity of the solar radiation falling on the array if the probe moves to a position twice as far from the Sun?
  Justify your answer.

Radioactivity

Exercise 10.1   Rutherford's Experiment

1. In Rutherford's famous experiment to investigate the structure of the atom, a beam of radiation is directed at a thin gold foil target as shown.

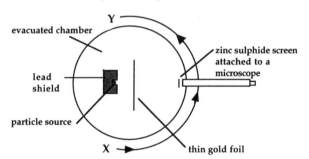

a) i)   State the type of radiation used.
    ii) Describe what the experimenters observed as the microscope was moved from X to Y.
    iii) Explain how the results of the experiment suggest that the mass of the atom is concentrated at its centre (the nucleus).
b) Geiger and Marsden carried out the experiment and also investigated the effect of using elements other than gold.
    By imagining the passage of a single particle near to the nucleus of an atom with an atomic number less than gold, suggest how the deflection might compare with a particle passing at the same distance from the nucleus of a gold atom.
    Explain your answer.

2. Describe briefly, with the aid of a diagram, the model of the atom which Rutherford proposed on the basis of the experiment described in question 1.

3. Decide whether or not each of the following are valid conclusions resulting from Rutherford's particle scattering experiment.

    a) The nucleus of an atom contains only neutrons and protons.
    b) The mass of the proton is nearly equal to that of the neutron.
    c) The nucleus of an atom is very much smaller than the atom itself.
    d) Alpha particles are helium nuclei.
    e) There are large spaces between the atoms in a gold foil.
    f) The nucleus has a very high density.
    g) The nucleus contains uncharged particles called neutrons.
    h) The nucleus has a positive charge.
    i) The alpha particles are absorbed, changing the atomic number of the metal.

Exercise 10.2   Alpha, Beta and Gamma

(A copy of the Periodic Table is required for the questions in this exercise.)

1. A radioactive source is known to emit two types of radiation.

    Describe, with the aid of a diagram, an experiment on the absorption of radiation which would allow you to determine which radiations are emitted.

2. A radioactive source emits radiation which is reduced to one third of its intensity when a sheet of notepaper is placed in front of the source, and is reduced almost to zero when a sheet of aluminium, 1 cm thick, is placed between the source and the counter.

    What types of radiation are emitted?

3. A radioactive source gives a high count rate when a Geiger-Muller detector is placed near it. The count rate drops appreciably when a sheet of paper is placed between the source and the detector. A sheet of lead, a few millimetres thick, in place of the paper causes no further appreciable drop but a sheet of lead, several centimetres thick, does cause a further drop in the count rate.

    a) What **two** types of radiation are emitted?
       Explain your answer.
    b) Why is there a very small count-rate, even with the lead screen in position?

4. A uranium atom has the symbol $^{238}_{92}U$.
    a) How many protons are in the nucleus
    b) How many neutrons are in the nucleus.
    c) How many electrons are in the neutral atom.

5. The two isotopes of chlorine have relative atomic masses of 35 and 37.
    a) What is meant by isotopes?
    b) Explain why the relative atomic mass of chlorine is quoted as 35.5.

6. a) What is meant by the term 'ionisation'?
    b) Which radiation, alpha, beta or gamma, produces the most ionisation?

7. Decide whether each of the following statements concerning gamma rays is true or false.
    a) They can ionise air.
    b) They can be deflected by electric fields.
    c) They can be deflected by magnetic fields.
    d) When a gamma ray is emitted, the nucleus changes into a different isotope.

8. a) Describe the structure of
       i)   an alpha particle,
       ii) a beta particle.
    b) What is a gamma ray?

9. For each of the following emissions, give the structure of the final daughter product.

    a) An atom of the radioactive isotope $^{234}_{91}Pa$ emits a beta particle.
    b) The nuclide $^{220}_{86}Rn$ emits an alpha particle.
    c) The radioisotope $^{237}_{93}Np$ emits an alpha particle.
    d) The radioactive nucleus $^{238}_{94}Pu$ emits a gamma ray.

10. Part of a radioactive decay chain is shown.

$$^{238}_{92}U \xrightarrow{\textbf{x}} \ ^{234}_{90}Th \xrightarrow{\textbf{y}} \ ^{234}_{91}Pa \xrightarrow{\textbf{z}} \ ^{234}_{92}U$$

Identify the particles emitted at stages **x**, **y** and **z**.

11. A decay series starting with thorium, $^{232}_{90}Th$, involves the emission in turn of alpha, beta, beta, gamma and alpha radiation.

Identify the final product.

12. What **three** particles must be emitted to change $^{238}_{92}U$ into $^{234}_{92}U$?

13. A radioactive element of atomic number **Z** and mass number **A** emits an alpha particle followed by a gamma ray.

What is the atomic number and the mass number of the new element formed?

14. The diagram shows a series of radioactive changes in which nucleus **W** forms nucleus **X** which then forms **Y** and finally **Z**.

a) What is the total change in mass number?
b) What is the total change in nuclear charge?

15. Part of a radioactive decay series of lead-212 is shown.

Give the element symbols with atomic number and mass number for each nuclide **X** and **Y**.

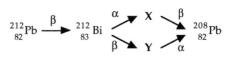

16. The unstable isotope of iodine, $^{139}_{53}I$, is a possible fission product in a nuclear reactor. It decays in **four** stages, emitting a beta particle each time.

a) Identify the nuclide formed as the stable end product, after the four stages.
b) The emitted beta particles carry away some energy as kinetic energy and at the same time energy is radiated from the nucleus in another form.
What name is given to this other form of radiation?

17. The last two stages in a radioactive decay series are shown. A bismuth nucleus decays by beta decay into polonium which then emits an alpha particle to form lead. Which numbers are represented by **P, Q, R** and **S**?

$$^{P}_{Q}Bi \xrightarrow{\beta} \ ^{R}_{S}Po \xrightarrow{\alpha} \ ^{208}_{82}Pb$$

18. Part of a radioactive decay series is:

$$^{235}_{92}U \xrightarrow{\textbf{x}} \ ^{231}_{90}Th \xrightarrow{\textbf{y}} \ ^{231}_{91}Pa \xrightarrow{\textbf{z}} \ ^{227}_{89}Ac \ldots\ldots\ldots \ ^{207}_{82}Pb$$

a) Name the types of radiation **x**, **y** and **z** .
b) How many alpha and beta particles are emitted in the missing part of the series, between actinium-227 and lead-207?
c) Explain why the series as given does not necessarily give a complete picture of the radiations emitted by each radioactive nucleus.

Exercise 10.3   Absorbed Dose and Dose Equivalent

1. A patients's thyroid gland is to receive a radiation dose of 500 Gy from a source, so that 15 J of energy is absorbed by the gland.
   Calculate the mass of the thyroid gland.

2. A stream of neutrons, of quality factor 10, produces a dose equivalent of 5 mSv in a biological specimen.
   Calculate the absorbed dose.

3   a) State the typical dose equivalent rate, in millisieverts per year, due to background radiation.
    b) Give **three** sources of background radiation.

4. Guidelines state that workers in the nuclear industry should not exceed 50 mSv in any year. Readings on monitors show that a particular area near Chernobyl will provide an absorbed dose rate of 1 mGy h^{-1} of gamma radiation, 200 µGy h^{-1} of thermal neutrons and 40 µGy h^{-1} of fast neutrons.

    a) Explain the meaning of 'absorbed dose'.
    b) Give **one** method of monitoring the absorbed dose that a worker experiences.
    c) State the relationship between dose equivalent and absorbed dose.
    d) Using the **Q** values given below, calculate how many days in a year a worker can be employed in this area if the worker is exposed to this environment for five hours per day.

Radiation	Q value
γ-rays	1
thermal neutrons	3
fast neutrons	10

5. In investigating the effect of different types of radiation on the human body, the data shown was obtained for one particular type of body tissue.

Radiation	Absorbed dose rate	Quality factor
gamma rays	100 µGy h^{-1}	1
fast neutrons	400 µGy h^{-1}	10
alpha particles	50 µGy h^{-1}	20

    a) Use the data in the table to show which radiation is likely to be the most harmful to this tissue.
    b) The maximum permitted dose equivalent for this tissue is 5 mSv.
       Calculate the time the tissue can be exposed to fast neutrons without exceeding this limit.
    c) A sample of this tissue has a mass of 25 g.
       How much energy will it absorb from fast neutrons in 2 hours?

6. A radium-226 source emits alpha, beta and gamma radiation with quality factors of 10, 1.3 and 1 respectively. The source is is stored in a steel cabinet and the absorbed dose rate 1 m from the cabinet is 0.0410 µGy h⁻¹.

   a) i)   Which radiation will **not** penetrate the walls of the steel cabinet?
      ii) Find the annual dose equivalent for someone working 1 m from the cabinet for 6 hours per day, 200 days per year.
      iii) State whether this exceeds the annual permitted dose for a member of the public.
   b) The worker considers this dose equivalent to be too high.
      State **two** ways in which it could be reduced.
   c) The biological effect of radiation striking a body depends on the energy absorbed by the body.
      State the **three** factors on which the energy absorbed by the body depends.

7. The workers in the factory assembling a smoke detector will experience an absorbed dose of 1.2×10^{-8} Gy for each detector assembled. The quality factor of this radiation is 20.

   Show by calculation whether or not a worker assembling 15 000 detectors in a year will exceed the permissible limit of 5.0 mSv per year.

8. A nuclear medicine laboratory contains a small radioactive source in a sealed container. The following information is displayed on the label.

Radionuclide: ^{131} I   Date: 7 th June 1999 (12 noon)   Activity: 300 MBq   Half life: 8 days   Radiation emitted: gamma (quality factor 1)   Dose equivalent rate at a distance of 1 m: 16 µSv h⁻¹

   a) When the source has the activity stated on the label, how many nuclei decay in 1 minute?
   b) A technician needs to work at a distance of 1 m from a freshly prepared source. For what period of time can the technician work at this distance so that the absorbed dose does not exceed 50 µGy?

9. In a sample of radioactive material 6×10^5 nuclei decay in a time interval of 1 minute.

   a) Calculate the activity of the sample.
   b) If each decay provides 2.5×10^{-16} J of energy to a tissue of mass 25 g, calculate the absorbed dose in 1 minute.
   c) If the quality factor of the radiation is 1.7, calculate the dose equivalent.

Exercise 10.4   Half Life

1. The activity of a radioactive source falls to one eighth of its original value in 24 minutes.

    What is the half life of this radioactive source?

2. A radioactive isotope has a half life of 20 minutes. A particular sample of this isotope gives a count rate of 3200 per second at 2 o'clock on a certain afternoon.

    At what time later that day is the count rate 200 per second?

3. In a half life experiment, the following readings were obtained.

Time	Corrected count rate
0 s	320 counts per second
40 s	160 counts per second

    What is the corrected count rate 160 s from the start of the experiment?

4. A radioactive element has a half life of 20 minutes.

    If we could study the decay of **one particular atom** of this material, what can we say about when this atom will decay?

5. In order to trace the line of a water pipe buried about 0.5 m below the surface of a field, an engineer proposes to add a radioactive isotope to the water. A Geiger-Muller detector will show an increase in count rate when held directly above the pipe.

    a) State whether the isotope should emit alpha, beta or gamma radiation.
    b) State whether the isotope should have a half life of a few minutes, a few hours or a few years.

6. The half life of radioactive sample is 8 days. The sample is held in front of a Geiger-Muller detector which gives a corrected count rate of 120 per minute. A second corrected count of 120 is taken 24 days later.

    For how many minutes would this second count have lasted?

7. Two radioactive substances are mixed together. Initially the count rate from each substance is 320 counts per minute, giving a total count rate of 640 counts per minute. The half lifes of the substances are 1 hour and 2 hours.

    What is the combined count rate after 4 hours, in counts per minute?

8. A radioactive source contains two materials. One material decays by the emission of alpha particles with a half life of 4 days, while the other material emits beta particle and has a half life of 3 days.
    The initial corrected count rate is 176 s^{-1} but this becomes 80 s^{-1} when a piece of tissue paper is placed between the source and the detector.

    What will be the corrected count rate (without the tissue paper present) after 12 days?

9. A counter measures the activity of a sample of radioactive element. The following results were obtained.

Time/s	0	30	60	90	120	150	180	210	240
Count rate per second	56	41	29	23	17	13	10	7	6

a) Draw a graph of count rate against time.
b) From the graph determine the background count rate.
c) From the graph determine the half life of the sample.
d) Explain why a background count rate of about 20 counts per second would have made it difficult to determine accurately the half life of this sample.

10. The sketch shows the apparatus used to determine the half life of a radioactive gas which is a member of the thorium decay series.

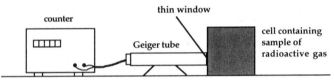

The counter is switched on for 10 s in every half minute and reset before the next reading is taken. The activity due to background radiation is 90 counts per minute. The results are recorded in the table below.

Time/s	0-10	30-40	60-70	90-100	120-130	150-160	180-190
Total count in 10 s	199	141	103	75	56	43	33

a) Use the results to plot a graph of corrected count rate in counts per second against time in seconds.
b) Use the graph to find the half life of the gas, explaining clearly how you arrived at your answer.

11. It has been calculated that it takes 4.5×10^9 years for half the uranium in a rock sample to disintegrate radioactively and turn into lead. The metals uranium and lead are contained in a particular rock sample. Of the atoms present in the metallic content, 30% are uranium and 70% are lead.

By drawing a graph of mass of uranium present or otherwise, estimate the age of the rock, assuming that 50% of the atoms in the original metallic content were uranium.

Exercise 10.5   Half-value Thickness

1. Sheets of lead of different thicknesses are placed between a radioactive source emitting only gamma radiation and a Geiger-Muller detector connected to a counter.

   Sketch a graph to show the variation of count rate with the thickness of lead.

2. Describe an experiment to show how the intensity of gamma radiation, transmitted through a lead absorber, varies with the thickness of the lead.
   List all the apparatus used and which measurements have to be made.

3. The half-value thickness for a particular material is 7 mm. A block of this material of thickness 3.5 cm is inserted between a radioactive source and some human tissue.

   What fraction of the original radiation passes through the block and reaches the human tissue?

4. Three materials **X**, **Y** and **Z** are used as gamma ray absorbers. They have half-value thicknesses of 2 cm, 4 cm and 8 cm respectively. Gamma rays of intensity *I* strike the left side of a 'sandwich' composed of **X**, **Y** and **Z** as shown.

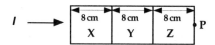

   Calculate the intensity at **P** as a fraction of *I*.

5. A detector placed near a source of gamma rays records a count rate of 480 counts per second. A slab of material of thickness 3 cm is then placed between the source and the detector. The half-value thickness of the material is 1 cm and the half life of the source is 1 day.

   After 1 day, what is the count rate recorded by the detector?

6. A worker in a nuclear fuel reprocessing plant is protected from gamma radiation by a screen as he sits at his work station. The absorbed dose rate at the work station is $40 \, \mu Gy \, h^{-1}$ of gamma radiation. The half-value thickness of the screen material is 8 mm.

   What extra thickness of screen material would be needed to reduce the absorbed dose rate at the work station to $5 \, \mu Gy \, h^{-1}$?

7. A source produces a dose equivalent rate of $32 \, \mu Sv \, h^{-1}$ at a distance of 1 m. Lead shielding with a half-value thickness of 3.3 mm is used to reduce the dose equivalent rate.

   a) Draw a graph to show how the dose equivalent rate at a distance of 1 m varies with the thickness of lead shielding.

   b) Use your graph to estimate the thickness of shielding required to reduce the level to $2.5 \, \mu Sv \, h^{-1}$.

8. Radiation from a nuclear reactor can affect human tissue. A health physicist is investigating the effect of a neutron beam and a gamma beam on some human tissue. A lead shield of half-value thickness 12 mm can be placed in the gamma ray beam. The following data is recorded.

Beam	Shield present	Quality factor	Absorbed dose rate
Neutron	no	10	$2 \, \mu Gy \, h^{-1}$
Gamma	yes	1	$5 \, \mu Gy \, h^{-1}$
Gamma	no	1	$40 \, \mu Gy \, h^{-1}$

a) Using the values from the table, calculate the thickness of the lead shield used.
b) Show that the dose equivalent rate of the neutron beam is 4 times that of the shielded gamma ray beam.

9. A patient receives radiation treatment from a radioisotope built into a plaster cast on his body. The radioisotope emits gamma rays. During the treatment, a nurse remains behind a lead screen. Without the screen in position the absorbed dose at the position of the nurse, 1 m from the patient, is 480 μGy.

a) What thickness of lead would be required to make the absorbed dose 7.5 μGy at the position of the nurse ?
(The half-value thickness of the lead for the screen is 1.2 cm.)
b) Without the shield, how far would the nurse have to stand away from the patient to reduce the absorbed dose to 7.5 μGy?

10. A certain radioactive source of gamma rays gives an absorbed dose in body tissue of $8 \, mGy \, h^{-1}$ when 1 m from the body tissue. During an experiment the source falls to the floor. The technician can retrieve it using tongs, with or without a lead shield of thickness 1.8 cm. The half-value thickness of lead for these gamma rays is 6 mm. Without the shield the retrieval would take 10 s, while with the shield it would take 40 s.

Show by calculation whether or not the technician would be advised to use the lead shield. (You may assume the distance between the technician and the source always remains at 1 m.)

11. A source of gamma radiation with a long half life has an activity of 600 kBq.
a) How many nuclei decay every second?
b) The source produces an absorbed dose of 512 μGy in some human tissue placed at a distance of 50 cm from the source.
  i) If a 24 cm lead shield is placed round the source, calculate the new absorbed dose. (The half-value thickness of the lead for the shield is 4 cm.)
  ii) Calculate the distance between the tissue and **unshielded** source if the absorbed dose is to be reduced to the value obtained in part b)i).

Exercise 10.6   Fission and Fusion

(A copy of the Periodic Table is required for the questions in this exercise.)

1. Energy is produced within the Sun by fusion reactions.

    a) State what is meant by a fusion reaction.
    b) Explain briefly why a fusion reaction releases energy.

2. A typical reaction produced in the core of a nuclear reactor can be described by the following equation.

    $$^{235}_{92}U + ^{1}_{0}n \longrightarrow ^{98}_{42}Mo + ^{136}_{54}Xe + 2^{1}_{0}n + 4^{0}_{-1}e$$

    a) State the name given to the above type of reaction.
    b) Large amounts of kinetic energy are released in this reaction. Explain how this kinetic energy is produced.

3. State the missing numbers, represented by **P** and **Q** in the following equation of a nuclear reaction.

    $$^{235}_{92}U + ^{1}_{0}n \longrightarrow ^{P}_{36}Kr + ^{144}_{Q}Ba + 2^{1}_{0}n$$

4. A possible nuclear reaction involving uranium is:

    $$^{235}_{92}U + ^{1}_{0}n \longrightarrow ^{x}_{52}Te + ^{98}_{y}Zr + 4^{1}_{0}n$$

    a) The symbol for the uranium nucleus is $^{235}_{92}U$. What information does this give about the nucleus?
    b) Determine the numbers represented by **x** and **y**.

5. A neutron source is made by mixing the beryllium isotope, $^{9}_{4}Be$, with an alpha emitting material. The beryllium isotope absorbs alpha particles and emits neutrons, one for each alpha particle absorbed.

    Write the balanced equation for the reaction identifying the nuclide that is produced.

6. There are three isotopes of hydrogen:
    hydrogen with no neutrons
    hydrogen with one neutron called deuterium
    hydrogen with two neutrons called tritium

    a) Write the symbol for each of the three isotopes in the form $^{x}_{y}H$.
    b) One deuterium nucleus combines with one tritium nucleus to form a helium nuclide, $^{4}_{2}He$.
    i)   Write the balanced equation for the reaction.
    ii) State the name given to this type of reaction.
    iii) Where is this reaction likely to take place?

7. A positron, symbol $^{0}_{1}e$, has the same mass as an electron but is positively charged. The nitrogen nuclide, $^{13}_{7}N$, decays by emitting a positron from the nucleus.

    Write a complete equation for the decay of $^{13}_{7}N$ and identify the radionuclide formed.

Exercise 10.7 $E = mc^2$

1. Various thermonuclear reactions take place in the Sun. One reaction is:

    $$_1^1\text{H} \; + \; _1^2\text{H} \longrightarrow \; _2^3\text{He}$$

    a) State the name given to this type of reaction.
    b) Use the information in the table below to calculate the energy released in the reaction.

Nuclide	$_1^1\text{H}$	$_1^2\text{H}$	$_2^3\text{He}$
Mass in kg	1.672×10^{-27}	3.342×10^{-27}	5.004×10^{-27}

2. The first artificial transmutation of one element into another was carried out by Cockcroft and Walton, who bombarded a lithium target with protons to produce helium as shown in the following reaction.

    $$_3^7\text{Li} \; + \; _1^1\text{H} \longrightarrow \; _2^4\text{He} \; + \; _2^4\text{He}$$

    The masses of the nuclei are: lithium 1.165×10^{-26} kg
                                         helium 6.647×10^{-27} kg
                                           proton 1.673×10^{-27} kg

    Calculate the energy produced in this reaction.

3. A plutonium-239 nucleus can absorb a neutron and then undergoes fission. The fission produces palladium-108 and xenon-129 along with some neutrons and some electrons.

Nuclide	$_{94}^{239}\text{Pu}$	$_{46}^{108}\text{Pd}$	$_{54}^{129}\text{Xe}$	$_0^1\text{n}$
Mass in kg	3.968×10^{-25}	1.791×10^{-25}	2.139×10^{-25}	1.675×10^{-27}

    a) Write a balanced equation for the reaction.
    b) Ignoring the mass of the electrons and using the data in the table, calculate the energy released in this fission reaction.

4. The equation for a nuclear fusion reaction is:

    $$_1^2\text{H} \; + \; _1^2\text{H} \longrightarrow \; _1^3\text{H} \; + \; _1^1\text{H}$$

    a) State the structure (number of protons and neutrons) of each of the nuclides in the equation.
    b) i)   Use the information in the table below to calculate the mass difference which occurs when the reaction takes place.

Nuclide	$_1^1\text{H}$	$_1^2\text{H}$	$_1^3\text{H}$
Mass in kg	1.672×10^{-27}	3.342×10^{-27}	5.005×10^{-27}

    ii)   Calculate the energy released in the reaction.
    c) Astrophysicists believe that the mass of the Sun is decreasing at a rate of about four million tonnes per second. Give an explanation.
    (1 tonne = 1000 kg)

5. Two possible nuclear reactions involving uranium , **A** and **B**, are shown by the equations.

A $\quad {}^{235}_{92}U + {}^{1}_{0}n \longrightarrow {}^{134}_{52}Te + {}^{98}_{40}Zr + 4\,{}^{1}_{0}n$

B $\quad {}^{235}_{92}U \longrightarrow {}^{144}_{a}Ba + {}^{90}_{36}Kr + b\,{}^{1}_{0}n$

a) What name is given to the type of nuclear reaction **A**?
b) What name is given to the type of nuclear reaction **B**?
c) State the numbers represented by a and b in reaction **B**.
d) The masses of the nuclei and particles involved in the reactions are as follows.

Nuclide	${}^{235}_{92}U$	${}^{134}_{52}Te$	${}^{98}_{40}Zr$
Mass in kg	3.901×10^{-25}	2.221×10^{-25}	1.626×10^{-25}

Nuclide	${}^{144}_{?}Ba$	${}^{90}_{36}Kr$	${}^{1}_{0}n$
Mass in kg	2.388×10^{-25}	1.492×10^{-25}	0.017×10^{-25}

i) Show by calculation the mass difference for each of the reactions **A** and **B**.
ii) Explain which of the reactions **A** or **B** releases the greater amount of energy.

6. The equation represents a typical nuclear reaction which takes place in a nuclear reactor.

$$ {}^{235}_{92}U + {}^{1}_{0}n \longrightarrow {}^{139}_{57}La + {}^{95}_{42}Mo + x\,{}^{1}_{0}n + y\,{}^{0}_{-1}e $$

a) Calculate the number of neutrons and beta particles released in this reaction, shown by **x** and **y** in the above nuclear equation.
b) Calculate the energy released in this reaction, using the following information but ignoring the mass of the beta particles.

Nuclide	${}^{235}_{92}U$	${}^{95}_{42}Mo$	${}^{139}_{57}La$	${}^{1}_{0}n$
Mass in kg	3.901×10^{-25}	1.575×10^{-25}	2.306×10^{-25}	1.675×10^{-27}

c) Estimate the electrical power produced by a generating plant which uses a nuclear reactor in which 1.0 kg of ${}^{235}_{92}U$ per day undergoes fission as above. The efficiency of the generating process is 40%.
(Take 1 day to be 8.6×10^4 s.)

Miscellaneous

Exercise 11.1   Uncertainties

1. When a ball is dropped six times, the rebound heights are:

    1.71 m, 1.78 m, 1.72 m, 1.76 m, 1.73 m, 1.74 m

    a) Calculate the mean value of the height of the bounce.
    b) Calculate the random uncertainty in this value.

2. The diagram shows the reading obtained
    on a voltmeter during an experiment.

    a) Write down the voltmeter reading and
    its uncertainty.
    b) Explain how you arrived at your value
    for the uncertainty.

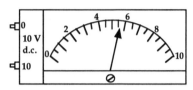

3. Measurements of the p.d. across a resistor and the current in the resistor give the
    following results.

    p.d.   =   30.00 ± 0.03 V
    current   =   2.00 ± 0.01 A

    Use these results to calculate the value of the resistance and express your answer in the
    form "resistance ± absolute uncertainty".

4. In an experiment to determine the specific heat capacity of a liquid, the liquid was
    heated in an insulated container using an immersion heater.
    The following results were obtained.

Heater current	=	5.0 ± 0.2 A
Heater voltage	=	12.0 ± 0.5 V
Time for which current flows	=	100 ± 1 s
Mass of liquid	=	1.000 ± 0.005 kg
Rise in temperature	=	10 ± 1 °C

    a) Calculate the value of the specific heat capacity of the liquid.
    (Energy required to heat liquid is given by E = mcΔT.)
    b) Identify which of the measurements given above has the largest percentage
    uncertainty.
    c) Determine the absolute uncertainty in the value of the specific heat capacity.

5. An experiment to measure the speed of sound gave the following results.

    Distance   3.000 ± 0.005 m
    Time   8.78 ms, 8.98 ms, 8.73 ms, 8.89 ms

    a) i)   Calculate the mean time.
    ii) Calculate the random uncertainty in the time measurement.
    b) From the results, calculate the speed of sound in air and the uncertainty in this
    calculated value.
    Express your answer as "speed ± absolute uncertainty".
    c) Suggest **one** way in which the uncertainty in the speed could be reduced.

Exercise 11.2   Mixed Problems

1. One million kilograms of water per minute flow through the turbines of a hydroelectric power station, after falling through a height of 50 m. The turbines develop a useful power output of 5 MW.

    Calculate the percentage efficiency of the energy conversion.

2. x and y are two physical quantities related as shown in the three graphs.

    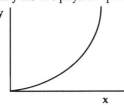
    a) y

    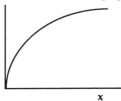
    b) y

    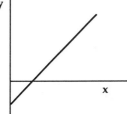
    c) y

    For each graph, state the most likely relationship between x and y .

3. a) Describe an experiment to investigate how the rate at which heat is produced in a coil of wire varies with the current in the wire.
    Include in your answer
    i)   a labelled diagram of the apparatus used,
    ii) a description of the experimental measurements made,
    iii) details of any measures taken to minimise experimental errors.
    b) In such an experiment the following results were obtained.

Rate of heat production/J s^{-1}	1.9	3.2	11	16	24
Current in wire/A	0.7	0.9	1.6	2.0	2.4

    i)   Use these results to determine the relationship between the rate of production of heat and the current in the wire.
    ii) From the above results determine the resistance of the wire.

4. Two pupils both measure impulse, one in kg m s^{-1} and the other in N s.
    Show that these two sets of units are identical.

5. Show that the units V m^{-1} (volts per metre) and N C^{-1} (newtons per coulomb) are identical.

6. What single unit can be used to measure 'force x velocity'?

7. The force of attraction **F** between two planets of mass m_1 kilograms and m_2 kilograms, a distance **d** metres apart is given by:

$$F = \frac{k\, m_1\, m_2}{d^2}$$

What are the units of the constant of proportionality **k**?

8. Read the following passage.

"In order to study very small objects properly, ultraviolet light is used because visible light bends round the object.
Viruses are so very small that even ultraviolet light does not show detail and instead a beam of electrons are used in an 'electron microscope'.
Even electron beams bend round tiny objects to a certain extent, so we cannot see any detail smaller than 10^{-10} m."

a) What do we call the bending of waves round obstacles?
b) Explain why ultraviolet light shows more detail than visible light in advanced microscopy.
c) Electrons are normally considered as tiny particles.
What does the above short passage imply about them?

9. An a.c. supply is connected through a transformer to a diode as shown.

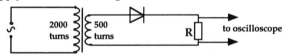

The input voltage is shown in the diagram.

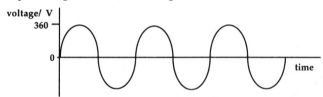

Sketch the resulting voltage output across **R**.

10. In a school workshop, a small transformer is used to operate an electric drill from the 230 V, 50 Hz mains. The voltage across the drill is 120 V and the current through it is 2 A (both r.m.s).

Assuming no energy losses in the coil of the transformer, what is the peak current in the primary?

11. A photocell is illuminated with monochromatic light. The photocell is made with a material which has a work function of 2.8×10^{-19} J.
The wavelength of the light is measured using a diffraction grating with 600 lines per millimetre. The first order line is found at 4.85°.

a) Calculate the wavelength of light used.
b) Calculate the frequency of light used.
c) Show by calculation, whether the light will be able to remove electrons from the surface of the photocell.
d) State the approximate range of wavelengths of visible light and state the colours which correspond to the wavelengths near each end of the spectrum.
e) Hence show whether the photocell will work within the visible spectrum.

12. A number of photodiodes are connected together and used in the photovoltaic mode to act as a solar cell. The following data is available for the cell.

maximum voltage available $= 0.5$ V
maximum current available $= 30$ mA cm^{-2}
efficiency $= 15\,\%$

a) Explain how a photodiode is constructed.
b) Explain how a photodiode is able to convert light into electrical energy.
c) Calculate the area of the solar cell, in square metres, if it is able to supply a maximum of 10 W of electrical power.
d) Calculate the energy from the Sun falling on the solar cell each second.
e) The sunlight is allowed to fall on a prism as shown.

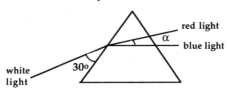

Find the size of the angle α if the refractive index of red light is 1.50 and that of blue light is 1.53 for the prism used.

13. Water enters the heater unit of a shower at a temperature of 5 °C and emerges from the shower head at a temperature of 44 °C. The water passing through the shower is collected for a period of 15 s and the mass of water is measured. This is repeated several times giving the following results.

mass of water   580 g, 572 g, 594 g, 554 g

Calculate the rate, in watts, at which the water gains energy, including an estimate of the uncertainty caused by the mass measurement.
(Energy required to heat water is given by $E = mc\Delta T$, where $c = 4180$ J kg^{-1} °C^{-1}.)

14. The apparatus in the sketch (**not** to scale) shows a pupil's attempt to measure the efficiency of a light bulb marked 250 W, 230 V.

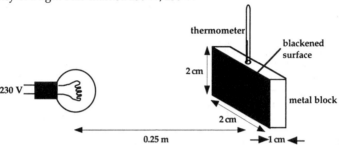

The metal block measured 2 cm x 2 cm x 1 cm and has a mass of 0.036 kg. It was blackened on the side facing the bulb and set 0.25 m from the centre of the bulb. The bulb was switched on for 4 minutes and it was found that the temperature of the block rose from 18.20 °C to 19.50 °C.

a) Calculate the quantity of heat absorbed by the block in the 4 minutes.
(Energy required to heat the block is given by E = mcΔT, where c = 400 J kg^{-1} °C^{-1}.)

b) Estimate, therefore, the total **heat** energy radiated from the bulb in 1 s.
(Surface area of a sphere is $4\pi r^2$ and π = 3.14.)

c) If it is assumed that the energy not radiated as heat is converted into light, how much energy is converted into light in 1 s?

d) Hence calculate the percentage efficiency of the bulb as a light source.

e) State **three** factors which have **not** been taken into consideration and say how each one could affect the result.

f) Explain why the side of the metal block facing the bulb is blackened and why it would be inadvisable to blacken the other sides as well.

15. It is said that when James Joule was on honeymoon in Switzerland, he investigated the conversion of potential energy to heat by attempting to detect a difference in the water temperature between the top and bottom of a waterfall.

a) i) Calculate the maximum temperature difference he could have expected for a 50 m high waterfall.
(Energy required to heat water is given by E = mcΔT, where c = 4180 J kg^{-1} °C^{-1}.)

ii) Explain why the temperature difference would not be this great.

b) i) In order to measure this difference in temperature he used a very sensitive mercury in glass thermometer.
Explain what is meant by 'sensitive' in this context.

ii) How would a mercury in glass thermometer be designed to be sensitive?